ISBN
9780444407177

£11·00

W0009769

ELSEVIER'S

DICTIONARY OF HYDROGEOLOGY

ELSEVIER'S DICTIONARY OF HYDROGEOLOGY

In Three Languages
English . French . German

COMPILED AND ARRANGED ON
AN ENGLISH ALPHABETICAL BASIS BY

HANS-OLAF PFANNKUCH

Associate Professor, Department of Geology and Geophysics,
University of Minnesota, Minneapolis, U.S.A.

ELSEVIER PUBLISHING COMPANY
AMSTERDAM/LONDON/NEW YORK
1969

DISTRIBUTION OF THIS ELSEVIER DICTIONARY
IS BEING HANDLED BY THE FOLLOWING
TEAM OF PUBLISHERS:

for the U.S.A. and Canada:
AMERICAN ELSEVIER PUBLISHING COMPANY, INC., NEW YORK

for Great Britain:
ELSEVIER PUBLISHING COMPANY, LTD., BARKING, ESSEX

for all remaining areas:
ELSEVIER PUBLISHING COMPANY, AMSTERDAM

First printed 1969
First reprinted 1971

Standard Book Number 444-40717-0

Library of Congress Card Number 67-19852

PRINTED IN THE NETHERLANDS

To my father
Johannes Pfannkuch

PREFACE

Hydrogeology, in its older and more restricted definition, deals with the occurrence and movement of ground water within the subsurface environment and its interrelation with the geological framework. It represents, however, only part of the hydrologic cycle which is the logical basis for all integral water resources planning. The modern hydrogeologist has to be thoroughly familiar with all aspects of the hydrologic cycle that directly influence the ground water situation. He has furthermore to be knowledgeable in ground water exploration, drilling and development techniques, as well as in the increasingly qualitative laboratory and analytical methods. In water resources planning and development, the hydrogeologist has to assume the role of the integrating generalist besides that of the specialist in his own field in order to bring together intelligently all pieces of information and to fit them into their proper place.

The aim of this dictionary is to cover the range of words and technical terms occurring in the field of hydrogeology proper, geohydrology, which deals with the analytical methods of hydromechanics in the geological and related laboratory context, ground water exploration through geophysical methods, aquifer development and exploitation through well-drilling and completion methods. Those parts of the hydrological cycle that have a direct bearing on the ground water situation are included, such as hydrometeorology, surface hydrology, hydrogeochemistry, and water quality. In recent years many new analytical tools, computer methods and laboratory procedures have been introduced or adapted from other fields in an interdisciplinary approach to the subject matter. It is only appropriate that the most frequently used terms be included.

The entries have been chosen from the English literature as cited in the bibliography and checked against the standard works in French and German. Terms were selected on the basis of their relevance and representativity in the principal categories and also according to frequency of appearance in the hydrogeological literature when they came from borderline and overlapping disciplines. In most cases an English definition is given to facilitate use and comprehension as well as to avoid ambiguities. Both standard works and specialized treatises of the subject matter were used as sources and reference. The English spelling is according to the American usage and follows Webster, the French Larousse, and the German Duden, with the exception of using ss instead of the β for typographical reasons.

The dictionary is intended for the hydrogeologist, hydrologist, earth scientist engineer and water resources planner, who have to keep up with the scientific and trade literature in the respective languages. Furthermore, it will be useful for those authors and information analysts who have to translate titles and abstracts of scientific articles in the field for the purpose of information dissemination and retrieval.

Although great care has been taken in selecting, defining and finding the equivalent French and German terms, certain omissions, ambiguities and errors are bound to occur in a dictionary of this scope. The author appreciates and encourages all suggestions, comments and criticisms pertaining to this dictionary. Last but not least, the help of Mrs. Marilyn Clarke for typing the manuscript, the author's wife for keeping the file, and Dr. Richard Davis for reading and discussing parts of the manuscript are gratefully acknowledged.

Saint Paul, 1969 Hans-Olaf Pfannkuch

BIBLIOGRAPHY

Andreae, H.: *Neue hydrometrische Verfahren*, pp.202, Oldenbourg Verlag, München, 1966.

Brinkmann, R.: *Abriss der Geologie: Allgemeine Geologie*, Band I, pp.286, Enke Verlag, Stuttgart, 1956.

Castany, G.: *Traité Pratique des Eaux Souterraines*, pp.657, Dunod, Paris, 1963.

Chow, Ven Te (editor): *Handbook of Applied Hydrology*, pp.1453, McGraw-Hill, New York, 1964.

Dadone, R.: *Notions sur les Diagraphies dans les Sondages*, Réf. 3030, Institut Français du Pétrole, pp.53, Ed. Technip, Paris, 1959.

Davis, S.N. and DeWiest, R.J.M.: *Hydrogeology*, pp.463, Wiley, New York, 1966.

DeWiest, R.J.M.: *Geohydrology*, pp.366, Wiley, New York, 1965.

v. Englehardt, W.: *Der Porenraum der Sedimente*, pp.207, Springer Verlag, Berlin, 1960.

Goguel, J. (editor): *La Terre*, pp.1735, Encyclopédie de la Pléiade, Librairie Gallimard, Paris, 1959.

Houpeurt, A.: Production *Etude des Roches Magasins*, Tome I, Réf.1093, Institut Français du Pétrole, pp.143, Ed. Technip, Paris, 1956.

Houpeurt, A.: Production *Mouvement des Fluides dans les Gisements d'Hydrocarbures - Essai des Puits,* Tome III, Réf. 2703, Institut Français du Pétrole, pp.229, Ed. Technip, Paris, 1958.

Keilhack, K.: *Lehrbuch der Grundwasser - und Quellenkunde*, pp.545, Geb. Bornträger, Berlin, 1912.

Keller, R.: *Gewässer und Wasserhaushalt des Festlandes*, pp.520, B.G. Teubner Verlagsges., Berlin, 1961.

Kettner, R.: *Allgemeine Geologie: Der Bau der Erdkruste*, Band I, pp.412, VEB Deutscher Verlag der Wissenschaften, Berlin, 1958.

Leliavsky, S.: *An Introduction to Fluvial Hydraulics*, pp.257, Dover Publ., New York, 1966.

Linck, G. and Jung, H.: *Grundriss der Mineralogie und Petrographie*, pp.290, Gustav Fischer, Jena, 1935.

Lynch, E.J.: *Formation Evaluation*, pp.422, Harper & Row, New York, 1962.

Maull, O.: *Handbuch der Geomorphologie*, 2nd edn., pp.600, Verlag F. Deuticke, Wien, 1958.

Meinzer, O.E.: *Outline of Ground-Water Hydrology*, U.S. G. S. Water Supply Paper 494, pp.71, U.S. Govt. Printing Office, Washington, D.C., 1923.

Meinzer, O.E.: *The Occurrence of Ground Water in the United States*, U.S. G. S. Water Supply Paper 489, Reprint 1959, pp.321, U.S. Govt. Printing Office, Washington, D.C., 1923.

Meinzer, O.E. (editor): *Hydrology*, pp.712, Dover Publ., New York, 1942.

Muskat, M.: *The Flow of Homogeneous Fluids Through Porous Media*, pp.763, J.W. Edwards, Ann Arbor, Michigan, 1946.

Nahrgang, G.: *Zur Theorie des vollkommenen und unvollkommenen Brunnens*, pp.43, Springer Verlag, Berlin, 1954.

Roche, M.: *Hydrologie de Surface*, pp.430, Gauthier-Villars, Paris, 1963.

Schoeller, H.: *Arid Zone Hydrology - Recent Developments*, pp.125, UNESCO, Paris, 1959.

Schoeller, H.: *Les Eaux Souterraines*, pp.642, Masson & Cie., Paris, 1962.

Thurner, A.: *Hydrogeologie*, pp.350, Springer Verlag, Wien, 1967.

Todd, D.K.: *Ground Water Hydrology*, pp.336, 6th printing, Wiley, New York, 1967.

Tolman, C.F.: *Ground Water*, pp.539, 1st edn., McGraw-Hill, New York, 1937.

Twort, A.C.: *A Textbook of Water Supply*, pp.422, American Elsevier, New York, 1964.

Vollmer, E.: *Encyclopaedia of Hydraulics, Soil and Foundation Engineering*, pp.398, Elsevier, Amsterdam, 1967.

Wechmann, A.: *Hydrologie*, pp.535, Oldenbourg Verlag, München, 1964.

Wundt, W.: *Gewässerkunde*, pp.320, Springer Verlag, Berlin, 1953.

Dictionaries

American Geological Institute, *Dictionary of Geological Terms*, pp.545, 2nd edn., Dolphin Reference Book C360, Doubleday & Co., New York, 1962.

Ketchian, S., Desbrandes, R., Dupuy, M., Pfannkuch, H.O.: *Dictionnaire Pétrolier des Techniques de Diagraphie, Forage et Production*, pp.334, Ed. Technip, Paris, 1965.

Meinck, F. and Möhle, H.: *Dictionary of Water and Sewage Engineering*, pp.449, Elsevier, Amsterdam, 1963.

Moltzer, J.: *Elsevier's Oilfield Dictionary*, pp.162, Elsevier, Amsterdam, 1965.

Visser, A.D.: *Elsevier's Dictionary of Soil Mechanics*, pp.359, Elsevier, Amsterdam, 1965.

Office of Water Resources Research, *Water Resources Thesaurus*, pp.237, U.S. Govt. Printing Office, Washington, D.C., 1966.

Duden, *Rechtschreibung der deutschen Sprache und der Fremdwörter*, 13. Aufl., Duden Verlag, Wiesbaden, 1952.

Petit Larousse, 22 tirage, pp.1798, Ed. Larousse, Paris, 1966.

Webster's Seventh New Collegiate Dictionary, G. & C. Merriam Co., Springfield, Massachusetts, 1967.

CONTENTS

LANGUAGE INDICATION – LANGUES – SPRACHEN

f	French	français	Französisch
d	German	allemand	Deutsch

ABBREVIATIONS

f	feminine	*mpl*	masculine plural
fpl	feminine plural	*n*	neuter
m	masculine	*npl*	neuter plural

BASIC TABLE

A

1 ABANDONED WELL
   f puits *m* abandonné
   d aufgelassene Bohrung *f*

2 ABLATION
   wearing away of ice or snow
   surfaces through evaporation
   f ablation *f*
   d Ablation *f*

3 ABOVE GROUND
   f de surface
   d oberirdisch; über Tage

4 ABSOLUTE ATMOSPHERE
   10^6 dynes per cm^2
   f atmosphère *f* absolue;
      atmosphère physique
   d absolute Atmosphäre *f*,
      physikalische Atmosphäre

5 ABSOLUTE HUMIDITY
   moisture content by weight per unit
   volume of air
   f humidité *f* absolue
   d absolute Feuchtigkeit *f*

6 ABSOLUTE POROSITY
   porosity established by taking into
   account all interconnected and non-
   connected or isolated void volumes
   f porosité *f* absolue
   d absolute Porosität *f*

7 ABSOLUTE PRESSURE
   f pression *f* absolue
   d Absolutdruck *m*

8 ABSORBING WELL
   recharge well, infiltration well
   f puits *m* de recharge
   d Versickerungsbrunnen *m*

9 ABYSS
   extremely great depth
   f abîme *m*; gouffre *m*
   d Schlund *m*; Abgrund *m*

10 ACCESSORY MINERAL
   mineral constituents of a rock
   occurring only in very small
   amounts
   f minéral *m* accessoire
   d Begleitmineral *n*

11 ACCLIVITY
   ascending slope
   f pente *f* ascendante
   d ansteigender Hang *m*

12 ACCRETION
   land addition by sediment deposition
   of a stream
   f remblaiement *m*; exhaussement *m*
   d fluviatile Akkumulation *f*;
      Aufschüttung *f*

13 ACCUMULATED PRECIPITATION
   f précipitations *f pl* cumulées
   d Niederschlagssumme *f*; Nieder-
      schlagsfülle *f*

14 ACCUMULATION
   building of new land by addition of
   sedimentary deposits
   f accumulation *f*
   d Anhäufung *f*, Akkumulation *f*

   ACCUMULATION, moisture see 2062

15 ACIDITY
   property of water with a pH below 4.5,
   caused by presence of mineral
   acids; expressed in equivalent
   amounts of calcium carbonate
   f acidité *f*
   d Azidität *f*; Säuregrad *m*

16 ACIDIZING OF WELLS
   improving well yield by pumping
   acids to clean walls or create
   solution channels
   f traitement *m* acide de puits
   d Säurebehandlung *f* von Brunnen

17 ACID MINE DRAINAGE
   acid waters originating from
   surface or underground mine
   workings
   f effluent *m* acide (venant d'une
      mine)
   d saure Grubenwässer *npl*

18 ACOUSTIC LOG
   log measuring speed of sound in
   rocks to determine porosity
   f diagraphie *f* sonique
   d Geschwindigkeitslog *n*

19 ACOUSTIC RESISTANCE
product of wave velocity and rock
density indicating the reflective
power of a boundary between two
strata
f résistance *f* acoustique
d Schallhärte *f*

20 ACRE-FOOT
amount of water which would cover
1 acre to a depth of 1 ft (326.000
gal.)
f mesure *f* de volume anglo-
américaine (1230m)
d Anglo-Amerikanisches Hohlmass
n (1230m)

21 ACTIVE GLACIER
glacier in active stage of growth
and movement
f glacier *m* actif
d aktiver Gletscher *m*

22 ACTIVE WATER
water with corrosive properties
f eau *f* active; eau *f* corrosive
d Aktivwässer *npl*; korrosive
Wässer *npl*

23 ACTIVITY COEFFICIENT
f coefficient *m* d'activité
d Aktivitätskoeffizient *m*

24 ADAPTER
f pièce *f* d'ajustage
d Passtück *n*

25 ADIABATIC
property of thermodynamic process
with no heat exchange
f adiabatique
d adiabatisch

26 ADJUSTED STREAM
stream flowing parallel to strike
of underlying beds
f rivière *f* subséquente
d subsequenter Fluss *m*

ADJUSTMENT, zero see 3028

27 ADJUSTMENT CURVE
f courbe *f* d'ajustage
d Ausgleichskurve *f*

28 ADSORPTION
f adsorption *f*
d Adsorption *f*

29 ADVECTION
phenomenon of cool air mass
intruding and interrupting evaporation and causing condenstion due to
heat loss
f advection *f*
d Advektion *f*

30 AERATION
introduction of air into water or
other liquid
f aération *f*
d Belüftung *f*

31 AERIAL PHOTOGRAPH
f photographie *f* aérienne
d Luftbildaufnahme *f*

32 AEROBIC
property of aquatic forms of life
existing only in presence of oxygen
f aérobique
d aerobisch

33 AGGRADATION
land addition through sediment
deposition
f remblaiement *m*
d Akkumulation *f*, Aufschüttung *f*

34 AGGRADING RIVER
river actively elevating its bed by
deposition of sediments
f rivière *f* remblayante
d akkumulierender Fluss *m*

35 AGGREGATE
grain mixture held together loosely
f agregat *m*
d Aggregat *n*

AGGREGATE, soil see 2589

36 AGGRESSIVE
quality of waters that attack metals
and concrete chemically by
dissolution
f agressif
d angreifend; aggressiv

37 A-HORIZON
topmost eluviated horizon of a soil
profile
f horizon *m* éluvial
d A-Horizont *m*; Eluvialhorizont *m*;
Auslaugungszone *f*

AIR, compressed see 332

38 AIR CONTENT
    f indice *m* d'aération
    d Porenluftgehalt *m*

39 AIR DRILLING
    drilling with air as drilling fluid
    for the transport of cuttings
    f forage *m* à l'air
    d Bohren *n* mit Luftspülung

40 AIR-DRY
    state of equilibrium between
    moisture held in porous sample and
    atmosphere
    f sec à l'air
    d lufttrocken

41 AIR HAMMER
    percussion drilling tool
    f marteau *m* pneumatique
    d Presslufthammer *m*

42 AIR LIFT
    method of lifting liquid column in
    a well by introducing air at the
    bottom
    f air-lift *m*
    d Lufthebeverfahren *n*

43 AIR LINE
    cable suspended above the stream
    water level (in discharge
    measurements)
    f câble *m* exondé
    d Luftseil *n*

44 AIR PRESSURE
    f pression *f* d'air
    d Luftdruck *m*

45 AIR RELEASE VALVE
    f clapet *m* à échappement d'air
    d Luftauslassventil *n*

46 AIR SEPARATING TANK
    tank in which desorbed gases are
    separated from the liquid and
    evacuated by pumping
    f séparateur *m* d'air
    d Luftabscheider *m*

47 AIR-VENT
    hole allowing passage of air during
    filling operations of closed
    reservoirs
    f trou *m* d'aération; trou *m*
       d'échappement
    d Entlüftungsöffnung *f*

48 ALBEDO
    ratio of reflected radiation to total
    radiation on a natural surface

    f albedo *m*
    d Albedo *n*

49 ALGAE CONTROL
    control of growth of micro-organisms
    in water bodies
    f mesures *f pl* contre les algues
    d Algenbekämpfung *f*

50 ALGAL LIMESTONE
    limestone formed by calcium
    secreting algae
    f calcaire *m* d'algues
    d Algenkalkstein *m*

51 ALGONKIAN
    geologic period of the Pre-Cambrian
    era
    f Éocambrien *m*
    d Algonkium *n*

52 ALKALI FLAT
    salt covered or heavily saline
    depression in arid environment
    f salina *f*; chott *m*
    d Salzpfanne *f*

53 ALKALI METAL
    f métal *m* alcalin
    d Alkalimetall *n*

54 ALKALINITY
    the property of water to neutralize
    acids expressed as calcium carbonate
    equivalents
    f alcalinité *f*
    d Alkalinität *f*

55 ALLOCHTHONOUS
    said of material originating from
    a different locality than the one
    where it is deposited
    f allochtone
    d allochthon; angeschwemmt;
       nicht bodenständig

56 ALLUVIAL APRON
    fan-like plain of glacial outwash
    deposit
    f cône *m* d'alluvions
    d Sandr *m*; alluviale Gletscher-
       ablagerung *f*

57 ALLUVIAL CHANNEL
    channel bed composed of
    unconsolidated alluvial material
    f chenal *m* alluvial
    d alluviale Rinne *f*

58 ALLUVIAL FAN
    fan-like deposit of detrital

material from steep mountain slopes
f éventail *m* d'alluvions; cône *m*
  d'alluvions
d alluvialer Schuttfächer *m*

59 ALLUVIAL FAN DEPOSIT
f dépôt *m* d'éboulis
d Fanglomerat *n*

60 ALLUVIAL PLAIN
plain formed by the deposition of
water borne sediments
f plaine *f* alluviale
d alluviale Aufschüttungsebene *f*

61 ALLUVIAL VENEER
very thin cover of water borne
sediments
f pellicule *f* alluviale
d dünner Schuttmantel *m*

62 ALLUVIUM
sedimentary deposits of streams
in relatively recent time
f alluvion *m*
d Alluvium *n*

63 ALTERNATING CURRENT
f courant *m* alternatif
d Wechselstrom *m*

64 ALVEOLAR
of a honeycomb shape; of certain
erosional patterns resulting in
cellular structure
f alvéolaire
d wabenförmig

65 AMMETER
current meter
f ampèremètre *m*
d Strommesser *m*, Ampèremeter *n*

66 AMORPHOUS SILICA
silica with no definite crystalline
structure
f silice *m* amorphe
d amorphe Kieselsäure *f*

67 AMORTIZATION
f amortissement *m*
d Stossdämpfung *f*

68 AMPHIBOLE;
HORNBLENDE
silica mineral
f amphibole *m*; hornblende *m*
d Hornblende *f*; Amphibol *n*

69 AMPLITUDE
half distance between the two

extreme points of a wave phenomenon
f amplitude *f*
d Amplitude *f*; Schwingungsweite *f*

70 ANALOG
physical or mathematical systems
obeying similar differential equations
with similar boundary conditions
as prototype such as network analogs,
electrolyte tanks etc. in ground
water flow problems
f modèle *m* analogique
d Analogmodell *n*

ANALOG, conductive-liquid see 342
-, conductive-sheet see 343

71 ANALOG SOLUTION
f solution *f* analogique
d analogische Lösung *f*; Analog-
  lösung *f*

ANALYSIS, chemical see 284
-, complete see 330
-, core see 388
-, frequency see 388
-, morphometric see 2078
-, physical see 2225
-, sieve see 2543
-, statistical see 2643

72 ANCHOR ICE;
GROUND ICE
ice temporarily attached to the
bottom of a river
f glace *f* de fond; glace *f* profonde
d Grundeis *n*

73 ANDESITE
basic volcanic rock
f andésite *m*
d Andesit *m*

74 ANEMOMETER
apparatus to measure wind speeds
f anémomètre *m*
d Windmesser *m*

75 ANGLE OF CONTACT;
WETTING ANGLE
angle between liquid phase and soli[d]
boundary measured through liquid
phase
f angle *m* de contact
d Randwinkel *m*; Kontaktwinkel *m*

76 ANGLE OF INCIDENCE
in seismic reflection method angle
between the incident seismic ray a[nd]
the normal to the surface of
reflection such as boundaries betw[een]

geological formations of different
acoustic properties
f   angle *m* d'incidence
d   Einfallswinkel *m*

77 ANGLE OF REFLEXION
in seismic reflection method angle
of the reflected ray with respect
to the normal to the reflecting
surface
f   angle *m* de réflexion
d   Reflexionswinkel *m*

78 ANGLE OF REFRACTION
in seismic refraction method angle
of the refracted ray with respect
to the normal of the refracting
surface
f   angle *m* de réfraction
d   Brechungswinkel *m*

79 ANGLE OF REPOSE
natural slope of unsupported granular
material
f   angle *m* de repos
d   Böschungswinkel *m*

80 ANGULAR
property of unconsolidated grains
with sharp edge
f   anguleux à arêtes vives
d   kantig; eckig

81 ANGULAR UNCONFORMITY
unconformity with marked
difference in dip of the superimposed
series
f   discordance *f*
d   Diskordanz *f*

82 ANHYDRIDE
anhydrous calcium sulfate, $CaSO_4$
f   anhydrite *m*; sulfate *m* de calcium
    anhydre
d   schwefelsaurer Kalk *m*; Anhydrit *n*

83 ANISOTROPIC
property of aquifer systems displaying different hydrological
properties in different directions
f   anisotropique
d   anisotropisch

84 ANNUAL FROST ZONE
top layer of ground subject to annual
freezing and thawing
f   zone *f* du gel annuel
d   jährliche Gefrierzone *f*

85 ANNUAL MEAN
mean value taken over all events

occurred during a year such as
precipitation, river stages, water
table levels
f   moyenne *f* annuelle
d   Jahresdurchschnitt *m*

86 ANNULUS
annular space between drill pipe
and casing or between casing and
walls
f   espace *m* annulaire
d   Ringraum *m*; Annulus *m*

87 ANOMALY
deviation from normally expected
findings, especially in exploration
geophysics an indication of change
in subsurface environment (i.e.
gravity-anomaly)
f   anomalie *f*
d   Abweichung *f*; Anomalie *f*

ANOMALY, gravity see 880

88 ANTECEDENT PRECIPITATION
INDEX
index based on amount of previous
precipitations
f   indice *m* de saturation
d   Vorwetterbeiwert *m*

89 ANTECEDENT-SOIL MOISTURE
degree of water saturation in the soil
prior to a precipitation event
f   teneur *f* antécédente d'eau
    dans le sol
d   vorhergehender Bodenwasser-
    gehalt *m*

90 ANTECEDENT STREAM
stream having established its course
before occurrence of orogenic events
altering general drainage pattern
f   rivière *f* antécédente
d   antezedenter Flusslauf *m*

91 ANTECEDENT VALLEY
valley established before
occurrence of orogenic movement
f   vallée *f* antécédente
d   antezedentes Tal *n*

92 ANTICLINAL VALLEY
valley established along the axis
of an eroded anticline
f   vallée *f* anticlinale
d   Satteltal *n*

93 ANTICLINE
upfolded stratum

f anticlinal *m*
d Sattel *m*

94 APATITE
phosphorite mineral
f apatite *m*
d Apatit *m*

95 APPARENT RESISTIVITY
f résistivité *f* apparente
d scheinbarer spezifischer
Widerstand *m*

96 APPROACH SEGMENT
part of hydrograph curve before
onset of precipitation
f segment *m* non-influencé de
l'hydrogramme
d unbeeiflusster Kurvenast *m*

97 APPROPRIATION
f concession *f*
d Verleihung *f*

98 AQUEDUCT
conduit to convey water, usually
above ground
f aqueduc *m*
d Aquädukt *m*

99 AQUICLUDE
impermeable rock stratum storing
but not transmitting ground water
f aquiclude *m*
d Grundwasserstauer *m*

100 AQUIFER
geological subsurface formation
containing and transmitting ground
water
f couche *f* aquifère; milieu *m*
aquifère
d Grundwasserleiter *m*

AQUIFER, artesian see 113
-, coastal see 314
-, leaky see 1147
-, tilted see 2790

101 AQUIFER STORAGE
gas storage in an aquifer
f stockage *m* de gaz dans une
couche aquifère
d Gasspeicherung *f* im Wasser-
träger

102 AQUIFUGE
rock neither storing nor transmitting water
f aquifuge *m*
d Grundwassersperre *f*

103 AQUITARD
semi-confining stratum permitting
some groundwater flow at a very
low transmission rate
f aquitard *m*
d begrenzt durchlässiger Grundwasserstauer *m*

104 ARAGONITE
instable orthorhombic carbonate
mineral, $CaCO_3$
f aragonite *m*
d Aragonit *n*

105 ARCHEAN
geologic period or the Pre-Cambrian
era
f Infracambrien *m*
d Archaikum *n*

AREA, drainage see 548
-, intake see 1048
-, overbank see 2153
-, wetted see 3009

106 AREA ELEVATION DISTRIBUTION
surficial distribution of elevations
for a given area
f répartition *f* hypsométrique
d Höhenverteilung *f*

107 AREA OF INFLUENCE
area over which effects of well
drainage are perceptible
f aire *f* d'influence
d Absenkungsfläche *f*; Einwirkungs
fläche *f*

108 ARGILLACEOUS
property of rocks containing clay
in non-negligible proportions
f argileux
d tonhaltig

109 ARGILLACEOUS LIMESTONE
limestone containing a considerable
portion of clay
f calcaire *m* argileux; marle *m*
d toniger Kalkstein *m*; Mergel *m*

110 ARID
property of dry climates and region
with a net deficiency of moisture
f aride
d arid; trocken

111 ARITHMETIC MEAN
f moyenne *f* arithmétique
d arithmetisches Mittel *n*

112 ARRIVAL TIME
time interval for first seismic
wave to arrive at geophone
f instant *m* de la première
   arrivée
d Zeitdauer *f* bis zum Anfangs-
   einsatz

113 ARTESIAN AQUIFER
confined aquifer where piezometric
surface rises above top of aquifer
bed
f couche *f* aquifère artésienne
d artesischer Grundwasserleiter *m*

114 ARTESIAN SPRING
water flowing under artesian pressure
pressure with piezometric surface
above ground surface
f source *f* artésienne
d artesische Quelle *f*

115 ARTESIAN WELL
free flowing well
f puits *m* artésien
d artesischer Brunnen *m*

ARTESIAN WELL, flowing see 756

116 ARTIFICIAL DISCHARGE
discharge of ground water through
pumping of wells
f exutoire *m* artificiel
d künstliche Grundwasserspende *f*

117 ARTIFICIAL RECHARGE
artificial replenishment of an
aquifer
f recharge *f* artificielle
d künstliche Grundwasserneubildung *f*

118 ATMOMETER
instrument to measure intensities
of evaporation
f atmomètre *m*
d Atmometer *n*; Verdunstungs-
   messer *m*

119 ATMOSPHERE
gaseous envelope of earth containing
and transporting air and water in
vapor and condensed form

f atmosphère *f*
d Atmosphäre *f*

ATMOSPHERE, absolute see 4

120 ATTRITION
wearing away of rocks by friction
f attrition *f*; usure *f*
d Abrieb *m*

121 AUGER
rotary drilling device where the
dry cuttings are removed continuously
by helical grooves on the drill pipe
f tarière *f*
d Erdbohrer *m*

122 AUGITE
silica mineral; pyroxene
f augite *m*
d Augit *n*

123 AUTOCHTHONOUS
of sedimentary material originating
and deposited at about the same
location
f autochtone
d autochthon; bodenständig

124 AVAILABLE WATER
water available to plants in soil
zone as defined by the interval
between field capacity and wilting
point
f eau *f* disponible (pour les
   plantes)
d nutzbare Kapazität *f*; ausnutz-
   bares Wasser *n*; pflanzennutz-
   bares Wasser *n*

125 AVALANCHE
snow or ice mass sliding or rolling
rapidly down a mountain slope
f avalanche *f*
d Lawine *f*

126 AZONAL SOIL
soils without distinct layering in
horizons
f sol *m* azonal
d azonales Bodenprofil *n*

B

127 BACKFLOW
 f reflux *m*
 d Rückfluss *m*

128 BACKGROUND NOISE
 level of intensity of signals due to
 normal activities other than the
 specific signal emission of especial
 importance in the interpretation of
 geophysical data
 f bruit *m* de fond
 d Störgeräusch *n*

129 BACKPRESSURE
 f contrepression *f*
 d Gegendruck *m*

130 BACKWASHING METHOD
 method of well development by
 repeated flushing
 f méthode *f* de lavage par contre-
  courant
 d Rückspülungsmethode *f*

131 BACKWASH WATER
 f eau *f* de rinçage
 d Spülwasser *n*

132 BACKWATER
 accumulated water above normal
 level of a water course due to
 impoundment at a point downstream
 f eaux *fpl* de remous
 d Rückstau *m*; Rückstauwasser *n*

133 BACKWATER CURVE
 water surface profile in stream or
 channel above constriction or
 impoundment
 f courbe *f* de remous; courbe *f* de
  retenue
 d Rückstaukurve *f*; Staukurve *f*

134 BAILER
 cylindrical container with bottom
 valve for the clearing of drill
 cuttings from the bottom hole
 f cuiller *f*
 d Sandpumpe *f*; Sandlöffel *m*;
  Schmandlöffel *m*

BAILING LINE see sand line

135 BALL VALVE
 f clapet *m* à billes
 d Kugelventil *n*

136 BANK
 ascending slope bordering a river
 (or lake)
 f rive *f*; berge *f*
 d Ufer *n*

BANK, high see 931

137 BANK EROSION
 erosion of a river bank
 f érosion *f* de la rive
 d Ufererosion *f*; Seitenerosion *f*

138 BANK STORAGE
 river water having infiltrated river
 banks during a high flow period and
 being retained in temporary storage
 f emmagasinement *m* dans la rive
 d Uferspeicherung *f*; Uferfiltrierung

139 BAROGRAPH
 pressure recorder
 f barographe *m*
 d Barograph *m*; Druckscheiber *m*

140 BAROMETER
 indicator of barometric pressure
 f baromètre *m*
 d Barometer *n*

141 BAROMETRIC EFFICIENCY
 ratio of water level change to
 atmospheric pressure change in a
 well
 f coefficient *m* barométrique;
  efficacité *f* barométrique
 d barometrischer Wirkungsgrad *m*

142 BAROMETRIC PRESSURE
 f pression barométrique *f*;
 d barometrischer Druck *m*

143 BARRIER
 geological formation or part of a
 formation having become impervious
 to ground water movement due to
 facies change
 f barrière *f*
 d Barriere *f*

BARRIER, fresh-water see 792
-, groundwater see 894
-, hydrologic see 973
-, permeability see 2206

144 BARRIER SPRING
     subsurface barrier forcing water to
     rise to surface and discharge as
     spring
     f source *f* de débordement
     d Stauquelle *f*

145 BASAL COMPLEX
     crystalline igneous or metamorphic
     rocks underlying sedimentary
     series
     f socle *m*
     d Urgebirge *n*; kristalliner Grund-
        komplex *m*

146 BASAL CONGLOMERATE
     conglomerate deposited on an
     erosion surface; conglomerate at
     bottom of a new sequence of layers
     f conglomérat *m* basal
     d Basalkonglomerat *n*

147 BASALT
     lava belonging to gabbro family
     f basalte *m*
     d Basalt *m*

148 BASE-EXCHANGE
     f échange *m* de base
     d Basenaustausch *m*

149 BASE FLOW;
     BASE RUNOFF
     sustained fair weather runoff
     f flot *m* de base; débit *m* de base
     d Trockenwetterkurve *f*

150 BASE LEVEL
     lowest level of erosion by a stream
     f niveau *m* de base
     d Erosionsbasis *f*

151 BASE LEVEL OF EROSION
     lowest theoretical level of surface
     to be achieved by erosion
     f niveau *m* de base d'érosion
     d Erosionsbasis *f*

152 BASE LINE
     arbitrary line from which deflec-
     tions of self potential are read;
     shale line
     f ligne *f* de base (des marnes)
     d Basislinie *f*

153 BASE LOAD
     f charge *f* normale
     d Grundlast *f*

154 BASE PLATE
     plate to seal off bottom of well
     f plaque *f* de base
     d Fussplatte *f*

BASE RUNOFF see
base flow

155 BASE WIDTH
     width of the hydrograph determined
     by a line parallel to the time axis
     cutting through the points where the
     rising limb starts and where
     recession curve ends
     f temps *m* de base
     d Basisbreite *f*

156 BASIN
     hydrogeographic unit receiving
     precipitation and discharging
     runoff in one point
     f bassin *m* versant
     d Becken *n*

157 BASIN CHARACTERISTICS
     physiographic geologic and ecologic
     characteristics of a basin
     f caractéristiques *m pl* du bassin
     d Beckeneigenschaften *f pl*

158 BASIN METHOD
     recharge method by spreading water
     in shallow basins
     f méthode *f* par bassins d'infiltra-
        tion
     d Sickerbeckenmethode *f*

159 BASIN MOUTH
     point at which runoff leaves a basin
     f exutoire *m* du bassin
     d Münduhg *f* eines Entwässerungs-
        gebietes

160 BASIN PERIMETER
     circumference of a basin following
     the divide
     f périmètre *m* du bassin
     d Beckenumfang *m*

161 BASIN SHAPE
     f forme *f* du bassin
     d Form *f* des Einzugsgebietes;
        Beckenform *f*

162 BATHOLITH
     very large body of intrusive rock

f batholite *m*
d Batholith *m*; Fussgranit *m*;
   Pluton *m*

163 BATHOMETER
instrument for measuring water
depths in wells
f bathomètre *m*
d Brunnenpfeife *f*; Grundwasserstandsmessgerät *n*

164 BEACH
shore consisting of sand or gravel
deposits
f plage *f*
d Strand *m*

165 BED
sedimentary deposit of relatively
small thickness and great areal
extent, separated by bedding planes
from over- and underlying deposits
f couche *f*; lit *m*
d Schicht *f*

BED, intercalated see 1053
-, lava see 1138
-, lower confining see 1171
-, marker see 1188
-, mortar see 921
-, river see 2418
-, stream see 2663
-, upper confining see 2873

BEDDING, cross see 414

166 BEDDING JOINT
joint parallel to or on bedding plane
f joint *m* de stratification
d Schichtfuge *f*

167 BEDDING PLANE
surface separating layers of
stratified rock
f plan *m* de stratification
d Schichtungsebene *f*

168 BED LOAD;
TRACTION LOAD
detritic material carried by stream
on or immediately above its bed
f charriage *m*; charge *f* du lit
d Geschiebefracht *f*

169 BEDROCK
solid rock underlying unconsolidated
material
f roche *f* solide
d Grundgestein *n*; anstehendes
   Gestein *n*; Anstehendes *n*

170 BED ROUGHNESS
roughness of channel or river bed
f rugosité *f* du lit
d Bettrauhigkeit *f*

171 BELL SOCKET
device for the retrieval of broken
drill pipe
f cloche *f* de repêchage
d Fangglocke *f*

172 BENCH MARK
fixed point used to mark elevation
with respect to an adopted datum
(especially for geodetic survey)
f borne *f* repère; point *m* fixe
d Bezugsmarke *f*; Höhenmarkierung

173 BEND
curve in a water course
f charnière *f*
d Umbiegung *f*

BEND, river see 2419

174 BENTONITIC SHALE
shale formed at the bottom of the
sea
f argilite *f* benthonique
d benthonischer Schiefer *m*

175 B-HORIZON
illuvial horizon in which soluble
material from the overlying
A-horizon has been deposited
f horizon *m* illuvial
d Illuvialhorizont *m*;
   B-Horizont *m*; Ausfällungszone *f*

176 BICARBONATE
HCO_3
f bicarbonate *m*
d Bikarbonat *n*

177 BIFURCATION
forklike separation of a water
course into two arms
f bifurcation *f*
d Flussgabelung *f*

178 BIFURCATION RATIO
ratio of number of stream segments
of a given order to the number of
segments of next high order
f indice *m* de bifurcation
d Verzweigungsverhältnis *n*;
   Bifurkationsverhältnis *n*

179 BIOCHEMICAL OXYGEN DEMAND
(BOD)

f   demande *f* biochimique en
    oxygène (D.B.O.)
d   biochemischer Sauerstoff-
    bedarf *m* (B.S.B.)

180   BIOTITE
      dark iron-magnesia mica
      f   biotite *m*
      d   Biotit *m*; dunkler Glimmer *m*

      BIT, core see 390
      -, cross see 415
      -, diamond drilling see 496
      -, drag see 545
      -, drilling see 572
      -, dull see 606
      -, jet see 1096
      -, pilot see 2234
      -, roller see 2433
      -, tricone rock see 2841

181   BIT CLEARANCE
      clearance between bit and bore hole
      sidewall
      f   jeu *m* du trépan
      d   Meisselspiel *n*

182   BIT WEIGHT
      weight exerted by string of drill
      pipe and drill collar on the drilling
      bit
      f   charge *f* sur l'outil
      d   Bohrdruck *m*

183   BLANK CASING
      solid casing without ports or outlets
      f   tubage *m* plein
      d   Vollverrohrung *f*

184   BLASTING CAP
      primary charge to set off detonation
      f   détonateur *m*
      d   Sprengkapsel *f*

      BLOCK, crown see 418
      -, pyroclastic see 2313

185   BLOCK AND TACKLE
      hoisting device in the derrick for
      lifting and lowering of drill pipe
      and casing
      f   palan *m*
      d   Flaschenzug *m*

186   BLOCK DIAGRAM
      f   diagramme *m* fonctionnel
      d   Blockbild *n*; Blockdiagramm *n*

187   BLOCKING
      f   blocage *f*
      d   Verriegellung *f*

188   BLOCK LAVA
      lava where broken fragments of
      solidifying crust form blocks
      f   lave *f* à blocaux
      d   Blocklava *f*

      BOD, see 179

189   BODY FORCE
      f   forces *f pl* massiques
      d   Massenkräfte *f pl*

190   BOG
      swamp
      f   marécage *m*
      d   Sumpf *m*

191   BORE
      f   trou *m* de forage
      d   Bohrung *f*

      BOTTOM, river see 2420

192   BOTTOM HOLE
      lowest part of a drilled hole where
      drill attacks rock formation
      f   fond *m* du puits
      d   Bohrlochsohle *f*

193   BOTTOMLAND
      lowland along alluvial river plain
      f   plaine *f* basse
      d   Flussniederung *f*

194   BOULDER CLAY
      unassorted mixture of glacial drift
      f   argile *f* à blocaux
      d   Geschiebelehm *m*

      BOUNDARY, fixed see 734

195   BOUNDARY CONDITIONS
      f   conditions *f pl* à la limite
      d   Randbedingungen *f pl*

196   BOUNDARY LAYER
      f   couche *f* limite
      d   Grenzschicht *f*

197   BOUNDARY SPRING
      spring located at boundary between
      permeable formation overlying
      impermeable substratum
      f   source *f* de déversement
      d   Schichtquelle *f*

198   BOURDON GAGE
      pressure gage with Bourdon tube
      f   tube *m* Bourdon
      d   Bourdondruckdose *f*

199 **BRACKISH WATER**
water containing from 1000 to
10000 ppm of total dissolved solids
f eau *f* saumâtre
d Brackwasser *n*

200 **BREAKING STRENGTH**
f résistance *f* à la rupture
d Bruchfestigkeit *f*

201 **BRECCIA**
rock composed of angular fragments
f brèche *f*
d Breckzie *f*

202 **BRIDGE CIRCUIT**
circuit of a current measuring
bridge
f schéma *m* de pont
d Brückenkreis *m*

203 **BRIDGING EFFECT**
forming of arches in a packing of
particles
f effet *m* d'arc-boutement
d Brückenbildung *f*

204 **BRINE**
water containing more than 100.000
ppm total dissolved solids
f saumure *f*
d Lauge *f*

205 **BRITTLE FAILURE**
f cassure *f* fragile
d Sprödbruch *m*

BROOK see creek

206 **BUBBLE GAGE**
stage recorder based on principle of
equating a gas pressure to water level
f limnigraphe *m* à bulles
d Druckluftpegel *m*

207 **BUCKET**
measuring reservoir in liquid
gaging instruments

f sceau *m*
d Eimer *m*; Sammelgefäss *n*

BUCKET, slush see 2576
-, tripping see 2797

208 **BUFFERED SOLUTION**
solution resisting changes in the
pH value upon addition of acids or
bases
f solution-tampon *f*
d Pufferlösung *f*

209 **BULK DENSITY**
f poids *m* spécifique apparent
d Raumgewicht *n*; Schüttgewicht *n*

210 **BULL WHEEL**
drum to store cable in cable tool
drilling
f tambour *m* de forage
d Bohrtrommel *m*

211 **BUOYANCY**
f poussée *f* d'Archimède
d Auftrieb *m*

212 **BURIED VALLEY**
ancient valley buried by recent,
often glacial, deposits
f vallée *f* enterrée
d verdecktes Stromtal *n*

213 **BURST**
periods of heavy rainfall
f pluie *f* torrentielle
d Wolkenburch *m*

214 **BUTTERFLY VALVE**
f vanne-papillon *f*
d Drosselventil *n*

215 **BYPASS**
f by-pass *m*
d Umgehungsleitung *f*

C

CABLE, carrier see 251
-, drilling see 573
-, hoisting see 936
-, logging see 1165

216 CABLE DRILLING
method of drilling where drilling
bit is suspended on a cable
f forage *m* au câble
d Seilbohren *n*

217 CABLE EYE
f cosse *f*
d Kausche *f*

218 CABLE REEL
f tambour *m* du câble
d Seiltrommel *f*

219 CABLE SPLICING
f épissure *f* de câble
d Spleiss *m*

220 CABLE TOOL
percussion, standard kind of
drilling bit
f installation *f* de forage par
battage
d Seilschlagbohrer *m*

221 CABLE TOOL DRILLING
f forage *m* par battage au câble
d Seilschlagbohren *n*

222 CABLE WAY
cable stretched across river with
cable car from which discharge
measurements can be taken
f transporteur *m* aérien;
téléférique *m*
d Seilbahn *f*

223 CAISSON
protective chamber for the
excavation of water submerged
unconsolidated sediments
f caisson *m*
d Caisson *n*; Senkkasten *m*

224 CALCAREOUS
containing calcium carbonate
f calcareux
d kalkig; kalkhaltig

225 CALCITE
stable mineral form of $CaCO_3$

f calcite *m*
d Kalzit *n*

226 CALDERA
circular volcanic depression
f caldère *m*
d Kaldera *m*

227 CALIBRATION
experimental evaluation of the scale
readings of an instrument against
an absolute standard
f calibration *f*
d Eichung *f*

228 CALIBRATION CURVE
f courbe d'étalonnage *f*
d Eichkurve *f*

229 CALICHE
indurated layer of soil, cemented
with leached calcium carbonate
f croûte *f* calcaire; encroûtement *m*;
concrétion *f*; alios *m*
d Felspanzer *m*; Ortstein *m*;
Kalkkruste *f*

230 CALIPER
device to measure inner diameter
of a well or drilled hole
f diamétreur *m*
d Kalibermessgerät *n*

231 CALIPER LOG
vertical record of well diameter
f diagraphie de diamétreur *f*;
diamétrage *m*
d Kalibermessung *f*

232 CAMBRIAN
oldest period of the Paleozoic era
f Cambrien *m*
d Kambrium *n*

233 CANAL SEEPAGE LOSS
water lost to underground by
seepage through channel bottom or
walls; loss through cracks in lined
canals
f perte *f* par infiltration
d Seihverlust *m*

234 CANYON
deep valley with steep slopes
f cañon *m*
d Canyon *m*

CAP, blasting see 184
-, drive see 589
-, hoisting see 937

235 CAPACITY
property to contain a certain
volume or a mass
f capacité f
d Fassungsvermögen n;
   Aufnahmefähigkeit f

CAPACITY, capillary see 716
-, carrying see 252
-, entrance see 655
-, exchange see 688
-, field see 716
-, field-carrying see 716
-, infiltration see 1025
-, self-cleaning see 2509
-, specific see 2614
-, storage see 2650
-, total see 2806
-, transmission see 2823
-, water retaining see 2619
-, well see 2983

236 CAPILLARITY
effect of surface forces in narrow
voids
f capillarité f
d Porensaugwirkung f;
   Kapillarität f

237 CAPILLARY CAPACITY
see field capacity

238 CAPILLARY FORCE
f force f de capillarité
d Kapillarkraft f

239 CAPILLARY FRINGE
zone immediately above water
table held by capillary forces
f frange f capillaire
d Kapillarsaum m; Porensaugsaum m;
   Saugsaum m

240 CAPILLARY HYSTERESIS
difference between displacement
and imbibition curve in capillary
pressure of soil tension curve
f hystérésis f capillaire
d kapillare Hysteresis f

241 CAPILLARY MIGRATION
movement of water through soil due
to capillary forces
f migration f capillaire
d Kapillarwanderung f

242 CAPILLARY RISE
phenomenon of natural rise of
water in small interstices, pores
and capillary tubes under attraction
of capillary forces
f ascension f capillaire
d Kapillaranstieg m

243 CAPILLARY WATER
water held by capillary forces above
water table in capillary fringe
f eau f capillaire; eau f de
   capillarité
d Kapillarwasser n; Porensaug-
   wasser n; Bergfeuchte f

244 CAPROCK
relatively impermeable rock overlying an oil or gas reservoir or a
gas storage site in an aquifer
f cap m
d Dach n

245 CAPSTAN
f cabestan m
d Winde f

246 CARBONATE
CO_3
f carbonate m
d Karbonat n

247 CARBONATED SPRING
f source f gazeuse naturelle (en C
d Kohlensäurequelle f;
   Säuerling m

248 CARBONATE ROCKS
rocks primarily made up of
carbonate minerals
f roches f pl carbonatées
d Karbonatgestein n

249 CARBON DIOXIDE
CO_2
f dioxyde m de carbone; dioxyde m
   carbonique
d Kohlendioxyd n

250 CARBONIFEROUS
geologic period of the Paleozoic
era, comprising both Pennsylvanian
and Mississippian
f Carbonifère m
d Karbon n

251 CARRIER CABLE
f câble m porteur
d Tragseil n

252 CARRYING CAPACITY
     capacity of a watercourse to
     transport solids
     f capacité *f* de transport
     d Transportfähigkeit *f*; Frachtungs-
        fähigkeit *f*; Schleppkraft *f*

253 CASING
     permanent liner of well
     f tubage *m*
     d Verrohrung *f*

     CASING, blank see 183
     -, pipe see 2237
     -, protective see 2298
     -, surface see 2713
     -, temporary see 2755

254 CASING JOINT
     welded or threaded connection for
     tubular casing
     f manchon *m* de tubage
     d Futterrohrverbinder *m*

255 CASING LINE
     cable with which casing is moved
     and put in place
     f câble *m* de tubage
     d Rohrförderseil *n*

256 CASING SHOE
     reinforced bottom part of casing
     to facilitate lowering operations
     and for protection of casing
     f sabot *m* de tubage
     d Verrohrungsschuh *m*

257 CATCHMENT
     drainage basin (British usage)
     f bassin *m* versant
     d Einzugsgebiet *n*

     CATCHMENT, water see 2928

258 CATHODIC PROTECTION
     method of corrosion prevention
     by electrochemical methods
     f protection *f* cathodique
     d kathodischer Schutz *m*

259 CATLINE
     cable connected to cathead for
     auxiliary operations
     f câble de cabestan *m*
     d Spillseil *n*

260 CAVE
     subsurface natural cavity of
     relatively great dimensions
     f caverne *f*; grotte *f*
     d Höhle *f*; Grotte *f*

261 CAVE, TO
     f s'ébouler; s'écrouler
     d einstürzen

262 CAVERNOUS ROCK
     rock containing many often
     irregular cavities
     f roche *f* caverneuse
     d kavernöses Gestein *n*

263 CAVERN WATER
     water contained in caverns
     f eaux *f pl* de cavernes
     d Höhlenwasser *n*

264 CAVING
     f éboulement *m*
     d Nachfall *m*

265 CEMENT
     technical bonding agent composed
     of finely ground sintered silica,
     lime and alumina; natural bonding
     agent
     f ciment *m*
     d Zement *m*

     CEMENT, groundwater see 898

266 CEMENT, TO
     sealing of exterior pipe or casing
     in a well to formation by a cement
     bond
     f cimenter
     d zementieren

267 CEMENTATION
     process of binding granular material
     together by deposition of cementing
     material at contact points of grains
     f cimentation *f*
     d Verkittung *f*; Zementation *f*

268 CEMENT BOND
     f adhérence *f* du ciment
     d Zementhaftung *f*

269 CEMENT GROUT
     cement slurry of pumpable consistency
     f ciment *m* d'injection
     d Einpresszement *m*

270 CEMENT SEAL
     f étanchéité *f* de ciment
     d Zementabdichtung *f*

271 CEMENT SLURRY
     liquid cement suspension
     f laitier de ciment *m*
     d Zementbrühe *f*

272 CENOZOIC
most recent geologic era
f Cénozoique *m*
d Känozoikum *n*

273 CENTRIFUGAL PUMP
f pompe *f* centrifuge
d Kreiselpumpe *f*

274 CENTROID OF STORM RAINFALL
center of gravity of area over
which rain is falling
f centre *m* de gravité d'une pluie
d Flächenzentrum *n* des Nieder-
schlages

275 CHAIN GAGE
water level measuring device
consisting of a chain
f jauge *f* à chaîne
d Kettenpegel *m*

276 CHALK
very porous, weakly consolidated
white limestone
f craie *f*
d Kreide *f*

277 CHANNEL
natural or artificial watercourse
bounded by banks
f canal *m*
d Kanal *m*

CHANNEL, alluvial see 57
-, stream see 2664

278 CHANNEL CHARACTERISTICS
hydraulic properties of stream
channel
f caractéristiques *mpl* du lit
d Flussbettbeschaffenheit *f*

CHANNEL FLOW, main see 1182

279 CHANNEL PRECIPITATION
direct precipitation on stream
channel
f précipitation *f* sur les surfaces
d'eau libre
d Niederschläge *mpl* auf Wasser-
flächen

280 CHANNEL SPRING
f source *f* de fossette
d Furchenquelle *f*

281 CHAOTIC STRUCTURE
f structure *f* chaotique
d chaotische Struktur *f*

282 CHARACTERISTIC HYDROGRAPH
hydrograph based on unit step
process
f hydrogramme *m* indiciel
d Indikatorhydrograph *m*

283 CHECK VALVE
f clapet *m* de fermeture
d Absperrventil *n*

284 CHEMICAL ANALYSIS
laboratory procedure in water
quality determination identifying
chemical constituents
f analyse *f* chimique
d chemische Analyse *f*

285 CHEMICAL DEPOSIT
sediment precipitated out of
solution by chemical action
f dépôt *m* chimique
d chemische Ausfällung *f*

286 CHEMICAL EQUIVALENT
expression of water characteristics
such as hardness or alkalinity
resulting from several ions in
solution in terms of only one
equivalent concentration
f équivalent *m* chimique
d chemisches Äquivalent *n*

287 CHEMICAL MOBILITY
tendency of an element to move in
a given hydrogeochemical
environment
f mobilité *f* chimique
d chemische Mobilität *f*

288 CHEMICAL OXYGEN DEMAND (COD)
measure of readily oxidizable
material contained in a water sample
f demande *f* chimique en oxygène
d chemischer Sauerstoffbedarf *m*

289 CHERT
amorphous silica concretion
f chaille *f*; silex *m* impur
d Feuerstein *m*; Hornstein *m*

290 CHISEL EDGE
f tranchant *m* de l'outil
d Meisselschneide *f*

291 CHLORINATION
addition of chlorine to water for
disinfection purposes
f chloration *f*
d Chlorung *f*

292 CHLORINE
Cl
f chlore *m*
d Chlor *n*

293 C-HORIZON
zone of weathered parent material
in soil profile
f horizon-C *m*; zone *f* de la roche
mère en voie d'altération; zone *f*
de départ
d C-Horizont *m*; Zone *f* des
angewitterten Ausgangsgesteins

294 CHURN DRILL
percussion drill
f foreuse *f* à percussion
d Schlagbohrer *m*

295 CIRCLE OF INFLUENCE
in radial flow circle over which
effects of pumping are felt
f cercle *m* d'influence
d Absenkungsbereich *m*

296 CISTERN
small water reservoir used to
collect surface and rain water
f citerne *f*
d Zisterne *f*

297 CLAM SHELL
excavating equipment
f drague *f* à grappin
d Greifbagger *m*

298 CLASTIC ROCK;
DETRITAL ROCK
sedimentary rock derived from
fragmentated other preexisting
rock or organic structures
f roche *f* détritique
d klastisches Gestein *n*

299 CLAY
soft plastic impervious rock
composed of clay minerals
f argile *f*
d Ton *m*

CLAY, boulder see 194

300 CLAYEY SAND
sand containing considerable
proportions of clay
f sable *m* argileux
d toniger Sand *m*

301 CLAY MINERAL
mainly hydrous aluminum or

magnesium silicates with a layer
type crystal structure
f minéraux *m pl* argileux
d Tonmineral *n*

302 CLAY PARTICLE
particle size less than 0.005 mm
(USBS)
f argile *m*
d Ton *m*

303 CLAY PLUG
fine flood deposits in a cut off
river meander
f bouchon *m* argileux
d Tonpfropfen *m*

304 CLEANOUT DRAIN
f trou *m* de vidange
d Ablassöffnung *f*

305 CLEAN SAND
sand with little or no clay content
f sable *m* propre; sable *m* pur
d reiner Sand *m*

306 CLEAVAGE
secondary planes along which rock
has a tendency to break easily
f clivage *m*
d Klüftung *f*; Spaltbarkeit *f*

307 CLIMATIC FACTOR
factor influencing hydrologic
parameters due to local climate
f facteur *m* climatique
d Klimafaktor *m*

308 CLOG, TO
action of blocking fluid flow paths
especially around a well bore
f colmater
d verstopfen; verkleben

309 CLOSED BASIN
drainage basin with no surface flow
outlet
f bassin *m* clos
d abflussloses Becken *n*

310 CLOUD
f nuage *m*
d Wolke *f*

311 CLOUDBURST
f pluie *f* torrentielle
d Wolkenbruch *m*

312 COARSE SAND
grain diameter 1 to 0.5 mm (USBS)

f   sable *m* grossier
d   Grobsand *m*

313 COARSNESS
quality of aggregates of un-consoli-
dated large diameter sand grains
f   grossièreté *f*
d   Grobkörnigkeit *f*

314 COASTAL AQUIFER
aquifer in coastal region open to
sea-water intrusions
f   couche *f*; aquifère *f* littorale
d   küstennaher Grundwasserleiter *m*

315 COASTAL PLAIN
plain adjacent to the seashore
f   plaine *f* littorale
d   Küstenebene *f*

316 COASTLINE
outline of the sea shore
f   ligne *f* de côte
d   Küstenlinie *f*

317 COATING
f   revêtement *m*
d   Überzug *m*; Auskleidung *f*

318 COCK
valve consisting of a rotating plug
f   robinet *m*
d   Hahn *m*

COD see 288

COEFFICIENT, activity see 23
-, drag see 546
-, field .... of permeability see 717
-, friction see 795
-, hygroscopic see 989
-, laboratory .... of permeability
   see 1113
-, pan see 2170
-, roughness see 2441
-, runoff see 2447
-, seepage see 2498
-, standard .... of permeability
   see 1113
-, storage see 2651
-, uniformity see 2867
-, unsaturated .... of permeability
   see 2869
-, weir see 2980
-, wilting see 3016

319 COEFFICIENT OF PERMEABILITY
f   coefficient *m* de perméabilité
d   Durchlässigkeitsziffer *f*;
   Durchlässigkeitsbeiwert *m*

COEFFICIENT OF TRANSMISSIBILITY
see transmissivity

320 COEFFICIENT OF VARIATION
standard deviation divided by mean
f   indice *m* de variation
d   relative Streuung *f*

321 COLD
f   froid
d   kalt

322 COLIFORM ORGANISM
micro organism the concentration of
which in a water sample indicates
the degree of organic pollution
f   colibacille *m*
d   Colibakterium *n*

323 COLLAPSE
f   écrasement *m*; effrondrement *m*
d   Einfallen *n*

324 COLLECTING MAIN
f   collecteur *m* principal
d   Sammelleitung *f*

325 COLLECTOR WELL
central well with horizontal sections
of screened collector pipe arranged
radially to increase yield
f   puits *m* collecteur
d   Sammelbrunnen *m*; Horizontal-
   brunnen *m*

COLUMN, geological see 828
-, mercury see 2026
-, mud see 2086

326 COLUMNAR JOINTING
jointing of basalt into hexagonal
vertical columns upon cooling
f   disjonction *f* en colonnes
d   Säulenklüftung *f*; säulenförmige
   Absonderung *f*

327 COMPACTION
volume reduction and lithification of
sediment due to compression
f   compaction *f*
d   Verdichtung *f*

328 COMPENSATION WATER
f   eau *f* de compensation
d   Zuschusswasser *n*

329 COMPLETE PENETRATION OF WE
property of a well that penetrates
an aquifer completely from the
upper confining bed or water table

to the lower confining bed; the
well is completed over the whole
thickness of the aquifer to allow
radial production over its entire
completed length
f   pénétration *f* complète d'un
    puits
d   vollkommenes Eindringen *n*
    eines Brunnens

330 COMPLETE WATER ANALYSIS
physical, chemical and bacterio-
logical analysis of a water sample
f   analyse *f* complète
d   Vollanalyse *f*

331 COMPOSITION
f   composition *f*
d   Zusammensetzung *f*

332 COMPRESSED AIR
air compressed to a higher
pressure than atmospheric
f   air *m* comprimé
d   Pressluft *f*; Druckluft *f*

333 COMPRESSIBILITY
relative change of volume with
pressure of water or aquifer
matrix; reciprocal of bulk modulus
of elasticity of a medium
f   compressibilité *f*
d   Kompressibilität *f*

334 COMPRESSION WAVE
f   onde *f* de compression
d   Druckwelle *f*

335 COMPRESSIVE STRENGTH
f   résistance *f* à la compression
d   Druckfestigkeit *f*

CONCENTRATION, hydrogen-ion
see 965

336 CONCENTRATION CURVE
rising limb on hydrograph curve
f   courbe *f* de concentration
d   Konzentrationskurve *f*

337 CONCENTRATION POINT
point at which all runoff of a given
area passes
f   point *m* de concentration
d   Konzentrationspunkt *m*

338 CONCRETE
f   béton *m*
d   Beton *m*

339 CONCRETION
localized deposition of mineral
matter going out of solution in
sediments or tuffs, usually of
nodular or irregular shape
f   concrétion *f*
d   Konkretion *f*

340 CONDENSATION
transition from vapor to liquid state
f   condensation *f*
d   Kondensation *f*

341 CONDENSATION NUCLEUS
small solid particle around which
condensation occurs
f   noyau *m* de condensation
d   Kondensationskern *m*

CONDITIONS, boundary see 195
-, geologic see 830
-, Ghyben-Herzberg see 844
-, initial see 1034

342 CONDUCTIVE-LIQUID ANALOG
analog using electrolyte in tank as
conductor
f   analogie *f* par cuve électrolytique
d   Elektrolyttankanalog *n*

343 CONDUCTIVE-SHEET ANALOG
analog using a sheet of electrically
conducting material with high
resistance as conductor
f   analogie *f* par tissu conducteur
d   Analogmodell *n* mit elektrisch
    leitender Schicht

344 CONDUCTOR
medium characterized by transporting quantities like heat, mass,
electricity
f   conducteur *m*
d   Leiter *m*

345 CONDUIT
natural or artificial duct for water
transportation
f   conduite *f*
d   Leitung *f*

CONE, talus see 2746

346 CONE OF INFLUENCE
depression created in water table
due to withdrawal from well
f   cône *m* d'appel
d   Einflusstrichter *m*;
    Absenkungstrichter *m*

347 CONE OF RECHARGE
elevation of piezometric surface
around a recharge well
f cône *m* de recharge
d Auffülltrichter *m*

348 CONFINED FLOW
f écoulement *m* de la nappe captive
d Fliessen *n* von gespanntem Grundwasser

349 CONFINED WATER
water separated from atmosphere
by impermeable rock stratum
f eau *f* captive; nappe *f* captive
d gespanntes Grundwasser *n*

350 CONFINING STRATUM
impermeable rock formation
preventing horizontal or vertical
outflow out of aquifer
f couche *f* imperméable
d undruchlässige Schicht *f*;
Grenzschicht *f*

351 CONFLUENCE
junction point of streams
f confluent *m*
d Zusammenfluss *m*

352 CONFORMAL MAPPING
transposition and solution of plane
flow problems in complex plane
f transformation *f* conforme
d konforme Abbildung *f*

353 CONGEALED LAVA CRUST
solid crust formed on top of lava
flow due to congealing action
f carapace *f* figée
d Erstarrungskruste *f*

354 CONGEALING PROCESS
process of cooling and solidification
f congélation *f*
d Gefrierprozess *m*; Erkaltung *f*;
Erstarrungsprozess *m*

355 CONGLOMERATE
rock consisting of large well
rounded waterworn particles
f conglomérat *m*
d Konglomerat *n*

CONGLOMERATE, basal see 146

356 CONJUCTIVE USE
use of both surface water and
ground water
f utilisation *f* jointe
d Verbundwirtschaft *f*

357 CONNATE WATER
entrapped residual water in
sedimentary rocks from time of
deposition
f eaux *fpl* connées
d ursprüngliches Porenwasser *n*

358 CONSEQUENT RIVER
river flowing down original slope
of geologic beds or general slope
of topography
f rivière *f* conséquente
d Folgefluss *m*; konsequenter Fluss *m*

359 CONSOLIDATED ROCK
rock that has become hard and
coherent through compression and
lithifaction
f roche *f* lapidifiée
d verfestigtes Gestein *n*

360 CONSOLIDATION
binding of grains by cementing
material to solid matrix
f consolidation *f*; lapidification *f*
d Verfestigung *f*

361 CONSTITUENT
f composant *m*
d Bestandteil *m*

CONSTITUENTS, trace see 2812

362 CONSTRICTION
f section *f* étranglée;
étranglement *m*
d Einschnürung *f*

363 CONSUMPTIVE USE
quantity of water used annually by
crops or natural vegetation due to
transpiration, tissue building, and
evaporation from adjacent soil
f consommation *f* totale
d Gesamtwasserverbrauch *m*

364 CONTACT LOAD
solid material in sliding or rolling
contact with stream bed
f charge *f* de la couche du lit
d Geschiebebelastung *f*

365 CONTACT LOG
resistivity log where measuring
electrodes are pressed against wall
of hole
f diagraphie *f* de contact;
diagraphie *f* de paroi; diagraph
de microrésistivité
d Mikrolog *n*; Kontaktlog *n*

366 CONTACT PLANE
     f   surface *f* de contact; surface *f*
         de séparation
     d   Grenzfläche *f*; Berührungsfläche *f*

367 CONTACT POTENTIAL
     electrochemical potential
     generated at the junction between two
     solutions of different concentration
     and a cation selective membrane
     such as a shale layer in S.P. logs
     f   potentiel *m* de contact
     d   Berührungspotential *n*

368 CONTACT SPRING
     spring at intersection of land
     surface with permeable water-bearing
     formation overlying less permeable
     formation
     f   source *f* de contact
     d   Schichtquelle *f*

369 CONTAMINATION
     introduction of objectionable or
     obnoxious material into water or
     waste water
     f   contamination *f*
     d   Verschmutzung *f*

     CONTAMINATION, radioactive
     see 2322

     CONTENT, air see 38
     -, moisture see 2063
     -, organic matter see 2137
     -, volumetric moisture see 2909
     -, water see 2930

370 CONTINENTAL SHELF
     continental margin extending under
     sea
     f   plateau *m* continental
     d   Kontinentalschelf *n*

371 CONTINENTAL SLOPE
     sloping part of continental margin
     f   talus *m* continental
     d   Kontinentalabsatz *m*

372 CONTINUOUS STREAM
     stream continuous in space from
     source to discharge point
     f   rivière *f* continue
     d   durchgehender Fluss *m*

373 CONTINUITY EQUATION
     f   équation *f* de continuité
     d   Kontinuitätsgleichung *f*;
         Kontinuitätsgesetz *n*

374 CONTOUR LINE
     f   courbe *f* de niveau
     d   Höhenlinie *f*; Höhenschicht-
         linie *f*

375 CONTRIBUTING REGION
     region contributing to well
     discharge in inclined watertable
     flow
     f   zone *f* d'appel
     d   Entnahmegebiet *n*; Entnahme-
         fläche *f*

376 CONTROL
     combined effect of channel charac-
     teristics (area, shape, slope, rough-
     ness) on rating curve
     f   facteurs *mpl* d'influence
     d   Einflussfaktoren *mpl*

     CONTROL, geologic see 831

377 CONTROL GATE
     f   vanne *f* de contrôle
     d   Kontrollschieber *m*

373 CONTROL VALVE
     f   vanne *f* de réglage; soupape *f*
         de commande
     d   Regelventil *n*; Steuerventil *n*

379 CONVECTIVE PRECIPITATION
     shower precipitation due to moist
     air being lifted over heated areas
     (thermal gradient)
     f   précipitation *f* de convection
     d   konvektiver Niederschlag *m*

380 CONVERGENCE
     net horizontal inflow of moisture
     per unit area
     f   convergence *f*
     d   Konvergenz *f*

381 CONVERSION FACTOR
     factor used to transform measured
     quantities in analog study to
     equivalent ground water terms
     f   facteur *m* de conversion
     d   Umrechnungsfaktor *m*;
         Umrechnungszahl *f*

382 CONVEYANCE
     physical characteristics of cross
     section of channel describing ability
     to transmit water
     f   capacité *f* de transport
     d   Transportfähigkeit *f*;
         Durchlassfähigkeit *f*

383 COOLING JOINT
     joint due to shrinkage of cooling
     rock mass
     f joint *m* de refroidissement
     d Erstarrungskluft *f*

384 COOLING WATER
     water used only for cooling purposes
     f eau *f* de refroidissement
     d Kühlwasser *n*

385 COOL SPRING
     spring water temperature below
     mean annual surface temperature
     f source *f* froide
     d Arkatopege *f*

386 COQUINA
     porous limestone composed of
     broken shell
     f lumachelle *f*
     d Schillkalk *m*; Muschelkalk *m*

387 CORE
     cylindrical plug of rock obtained by
     special core drilling operations for
     detailed geological studies
     f carotte *f*
     d Bohrkern *m*

388 CORE ANALYSIS
     petrophysical analysis of a drilled
     rock core sample
     f analyse *f* de carotte
     d Bohrkernuntersuchung *f*

389 CORE BARREL
     tubular part of core drilling device
     that contains the cut rock sample
     during drilling operations
     f tube *m* carottier
     d Kernrohr *n*

390 CORE BIT
     tubular and internally hollow
     drilling bit cutting cylindrical rock
     samples
     f tête *f* de carottier
     d Kernbohrkrone *f*

391 CORE CATCHER
     annular spring retaining core in
     core barrel
     f arrache-carotte *m*
     d Kernfänger *m*

392 CORE DRILLING
     drilling method producing a cylin-
     drical rock sample of the penetrated
     formation

     f carottage *m*
     d Kernbohren *n*

393 CORRASION
     physical erosion due to particles
     moved by wind and water
     f corrasion *f*
     d Korrasion *f*

394 CORROSION INHIBITOR
     chemical additive to water and
     drilling fluids neutralizing their
     corrosive properties
     f inhibiteur *m* de corrosion
     d Korrosionsverhütungsmittel *n*

395 CORROSIVE
     property of water attacking its
     conduits
     f corrosif
     d korrosiv

396 COUNTER CURRENT
     f contre-courant *m*
     d Gegenstrom *m*; Gegenströmung *f*

     COVER, mechanical see 2015
     -, snow see 2579
     -, vegetation see 2887

397 CRACK
     tight joint
     f cassure *f*
     d Kluft *f*; Riss *m*

     CRACK, dessication see 483
     -, mud see 2087

398 CRANK
     f manivelle *f*
     d Kurbel *f*

399 CRATER LAKE
     water body accumulated in an
     impervious volcanic crater
     f lac *m* de cratère
     d Kratersee *m*

400 CREEK;
     BROOK
     f watercourse of lesser volume th
     a river
     f ruisseau *m*
     d Bach *m*

401 CREEP
     slow plastic deformation of a solid
     f fluage *m*
     d plastische Verformung *f*;
        Kriechen *n*

402 CREEP FLOW
flow with creeping motion where
inertial terms have been dropped
f écoulement *m* très lent
d sehr langsame Fliessbewegung *f*

403 CREST
f sommet *m*
d Gipfelpunkt *m*

CREST, flood see 745

404 CREST LINE
line connecting crests (e.g. as a
divide)
f ligne *f* de crête
d Gipfellinie *f*

405 CREST SEGMENT
top part of hydrograph
f pointe *f*
d Spitzensegment *n*

406 CREST-STAGE INDICATOR
mechanical gage preserving the
indication of highest water level
f indicateur *m* de pointe;
échelle *f* à maximums
d Spitzenwertanzeiger *m*

407 CRETACEOUS
most recent geologic period of the
Mesozoic era
f Crétacé *m*
d Kreide *n*

408 CREVASSE
fissure in a glacier or other ice
body
f crevasse *f*
d Gletscherspalte *f*

409 CREVICE
opening in a rock formation or a
glacier
f fente *f*; crevasse *f*
d Spalte *f*

410 CRITICAL DEPTH
depth of flow in open channel when
specific energy is minimum
f profondeur *f* critique
d kritische Wassertiefe *f*

411 CRITICAL DEPTH FLUME
Venturi or Parshall flume for
discharge measurements
f jaugeur *m* Parshall
d Venturikanal *m*

412 CRITICAL FLOW
open channel flow with Froude
Number equal to unity
f écoulement *m* critique
d kritsche Fliessgeschwindigkeit *f*

413 CROOKED HOLE
bore hole deflected from the vertical
f sonde *f* tordue
d Schlüsselloch *n*

414 CROSS BEDDING
oblique deposition of thin beds with
respect ot main planes of stratification
f stratification *f* entrecroisée
d Kreuzschichtung *f*

415 CROSS BIT
drilling bit with the chisel edges
arranged crosswise
f outil *m* à section en croix
d Kreuzmeissel *m*

416 CROSS FAULT
fault oblique or at right angles to
strike direction of beds
f faille *f* perpendiculaire
d Querverwerfung *f*

417 CROSS SECTION
vertical section of a geologic profile
f coupe *f* transversale
d Querschnitt *m*

418 CROWN BLOCK
block at the top of a drilling rig
containing pulleys for the draw
works
f moufle *m* fixe
d Kronenblock *m*

419 CRUSHED GRAVEL
f gravillon *m* concassé
d Grobsplitt *m*

420 CRYOLOGY
study of water dealing with solid
forms of water
f cryologie *f*
d Cryologie *f*

421 CRYSTALLINE ROCK
rock constituted by minerals in
crystalline state, very often highly
impermeable
f roche *f* cristalline
d kristallines Gestein *n*

422 CUESTA
unsymmetrical ridge due to gently

dipping stratum; hogback
f   côte *f*
d   Schichtstufe *f*

423   CULVERT
f   ponceau *m*
d   Durchlass *m*

424   CUMULATIVE PRODUCTION
sum total of volumetric discharge
of a well since production began
f   production *f* cumulée
d   Gesamtproduktion *f*

425   CURB
upper part of well casing near
surface
f   revêtement *m*
d   Einfassung *f*

CURB, well see 2986

426   CURIE (C)
measure of radioactivity by disintegration; 37×10^{12} disintegrations
per second
f   curie *m*
d   Curie *f*

CURRENT, counter see 396
-, density see 462
-, earth see 614
-, stray see 2661

427   CURRENT ELECTRODE
in a well logging circuit the
electrode furnishing the current
f   électrode *f* de courant
d   Stromelektrode *f*

428   CURRENT METER
device to measure current velocity
directly at a given point
f   moulinet *m*
d   Stromgeschwindigkeitsmesser *m*;
    Flügelmessgerät *n*

CURVE, adjustment see 27
-, backwater see 133
-, calibration see 228
-, concentration see 336
-, desorption see 482

-, drawdown see 563
-, duration see 609
-, flow duration see 755
-, flow-mass see 758
-, groundwater recession see 908
-, lateral see 1132
-, mass see 1191
-, normal see 2113
-, pressure buildup see 2290
-, rating see 2342
-, recession see 2354
-, resistivity-spacing see 2400
-, summation see 2702
-, time-drawdown see 2792
-, type see 2855

429   CURVE FITTING
fitting of experimental data points
f   lissage *m*
d   Ausgleichung *f*

430   CUTICULAR TRANSPIRATION
evaporation from moist membranes
of plants
f   transpiration *f* cuticulaire
d   kutikuläre Transpiration *f*

431   CUTTING BLADE
cutting edge of a rotary drilling bit
f   lame *f* coupante
d   Schneide *f*

432   CUTTINGS
rock chips loosened from the bottom
hole by drilling action
f   déblais *m* de forage
d   Bohrklein *n*

433   CYCLE
regular periodic occurrence of an
event
f   cycle *m*
d   Zyklus *m*

CYCLE, hydrologic see 975
-, water see 2932

434   CYCLONIC PRECIPITATION
moderate precipitation in low
pressure area
f   précipitation *f* cyclonique
d   zykonaler Niederschlag *m*

D

435 DAM
structure across a watercourse
used to impound water
f barrage *m*
d Staudamm *m*; Talsperre *f*

DAM, groundwater see 899
-, overflow see 2158

436 DAMPING
process of gradually reducing
amplitude of a periodic event
such as acoustic oscillations in
velocity logging
f amortissement *m*
d Dämpfung *f*

437 DAMPING EFFECT
f effet *m* d'amortissement
d Dämpfungseffekt *m*

438 DARCY'S LAW
emprical law relating specific
discharge during fluid flow through
porous media to a permeability
coefficient K and a hydraulic
gradient
f Loi *f* de Darcy
d Darcysches Gesetz *n*

439 DARCY (UNIT) (d)
practical unit, measure of intrinsic
permeability has dimension of
L^2 in cgs system: 10^{-8} cm^2
f Darcy *m* (d)
d Darcy *n* (d)

440 DARCY VELOCITY;
SEEPAGE VELOCITY; SPECIFIC
DISCHARGE
ficticious flow velocity through
total cross sections area of porous
medium including solids
f vitesse *f* Darcy; vitesse *f*
apparente; vitesse *f* de filtration
d Darcy Geschwindigkeit *f*;
Filtergeschwindigkeit *f*;
Durchgangsgeschwindigkeit *f*

441 DATA
f données *f pl*
d Angaben *f pl*; Daten *f pl*

DATUM, zero see 3029

442 DATUM PLANE
reference level to which topographic
or water levels in well are related
f plan *m* de comparaison; niveau *m*
de référence
d Bezugsebene *f*; Bezugsniveau *n*

443 DEAD WATER
standing, stagnant water
f eau *f* morte
d Stehendwasser *n*

444 DEBRIS
coarse rock fragments resulting
from erosion and disintegration of
bedrock
f débris *m*
d Schutt *m*

445 DECAY PRODUCT
f produit *m* de désintégration
radioactive
d Zerfallsprodukt *n*

446 DECLOGGING
cleaning of clogged well surfaces
or screens
f nettoyage *m* de la paroi colmatée
d'un puits; décolmatage *m*
d Reinigung *f* verklebter Zufluss-
flächen

447 DECOMPOSE, TO
f décomposer
d zersetzen

448 DEEP WELL DRILLING
f forage *m* profond
d Tiefbohrung *f*

449 DEEP WELL TURBINE PUMP
f pompe *f* à turbine immergée
d unterwasser Turbinenpumpe *f*

450 DEFORMATION
changing of form, volume and
relative position of rock masses
f déformation *f*
d Verformung *f*; Formveränderung *f*

451 DEGRADATION
geological action of wearing down
a surface
f dégradation *f*
d Abtragung *f*

452 DEGREE OF AERATION
ratio of volume of air in sample
to sample volume
f degré *m* d'aération
d Belüftungsgrad *m*

453 DEGREE OF CEMENTATION
degree to which a rock has been
solidified due to cementation
f degré *m* de lapidifaction
d Zementationsgrad *m*; Verfesti-
gungsgrad *m*

454 DEGREE OF SATURATION
ratio of volume of water to volume
of pores
f degré *m* de saturation
d Sättigungsgrad *m*

455 DELAY
lapse time between signal emission
and signal reception in seismic
logging
f retard *m*
d Verzögerung *f*

456 DELTA
triangular deposit of sediments at
the inflow of a river into the
ocean or a lake
f delta *m*
d Delta *n*; Flussmündungsgebiet *n*

457 DELTAIC DEPOSITS
f dépôts *mpl* deltaiques
d Delta-Ablagerungen *fpl*

458 DEMAND
rate of draft from an aquifer or
reservoir to meet a certain demand
f demande *f* en eau
d Nachfrage *f*; Verbrauch *m*

DEMAND, oxygen see 2164
-, water see 2933

459 DEMINERALIZATION
removal of mineral matter from
water
f déminéralisation *f*
d Entmineralisierung *f*

460 DENDRITIC
tree-like pattern
f dentritique; arborescent
d verästelt; dendritisch

461 DENSITY
f densité *f*
d Dichte *f*

DENSITY, bulk see 209
-, drainage see 550
-, mass see 1192
-, snow see 2580
-, specific see 2615
-, weight see 2978

462 DENSITY CURRENT
current due to weight density
differences in the fluid under
consideration
f courant *m* de densité
d Dichteströmung *f*; konvektive
Strömung *f*

463 DENUDATION
wearing away of overlying loose
rock to top of bedrock
f dénudation *f*
d Abtragung *f*; Denudation *f*;
Massenabtrag *m*; Landerniedrigung

464 DEPARTURE
in SP logging deflection from the
base (shale) line
f anomalie *f* de la courbe PS
d Abweichung *f* von der Basislinie
der SP Kurve; Eindringung *f*

465 DEPLETION
withdrawal of water at a greater
rate than replenishment
f épuisement *m*
d Vorratsverminderung *f*;
Erschöpfung *f*

DEPOSIT, alluvial fan see 59
-, chemical see 285
-, eolian see 658
-, glacial see 845
-, moraine see 2077
-, organic see 2136
-, point-bar see 2255
-, sedimentary see 2494

466 DEPOSITION FACTOR
factor describing settling of
suspended solid within pore space
f facteur *m* de déposition
d Absetzfaktor *m*

DEPOSITS, deltaic see 457

467 DEPRESSION
small hollow in a surface
f dépression *f*
d Vertiefung *f*

468 DEPRESSION SPRING
spring originating at intersection o
land surface with water table
f source *f* de dépression
d Muldenquelle *f*

DEPTH, critical see 410
-, invasion see 1077
-, normal see 2114
-, transpiration see 2826

DEPTH FLUME, critical see 411

469 DEPTH GAGE
a) any device to measure depths
as to water level in well, etc.
b) spec.: gage for the measurement
of the river stage
f a) jauge *f* de profondeur
   b) jauge *f* fluviale
d a) Tiefenanzeiger *m*
   b) Pegel *m*

470 DEPTH OF EVAPORATION
f hauteur *f* d'évaporation
d Verdunstungshöhe *f*

471 DEPTH OF PENETRATION
depth to which electrical field
penetrates into subsurface as a
function of electrode spacing
f profondeur *f* de pénétration
d Eindringungstiefe *f*

472 DEPTH OF PRECIPITATION
f hauteur *f* de précipitation
d Niederschlagshöhe *f*

473 DEPTH OF RAINFALL
f hauteur *f* pluviométrique
d Regenhöhe *f*

474 DEPTH OF SNOW
f profondeur *f* de la neige
d Schneetiefe *f*

475 DERRICK
frame structure containing hoisting
devices in a drilling installation
f derrick *m*
d Bohrturm *m*

476 DESALINATION
process of salt removal
f dessalage *m*
d Entsalzung *f*

477 DESANDER
device for the separation of sand
from well water
f dessableur *m*
d Sandabscheider *m*

478 DESERT
region where net moisture inflow is
too small to support any vegetation
f désert *m*
d Wüste *f*

479 DESICCATION
removal of moisture by evaporation,
drying
f dessiccation *f*; séchage *m*
d Austrocknung *f*; Trocknen *n*

480 DESIGN FLOOD
most severe flood to be entered
in design calculations for engineering
works
f crue *f* utilisée pour un calcul
d Hochwasserberechnungsgrund-
lage *f*

481 DESIGN STORM
most severe storm used as base for
hydrologic and engineering designs
f averse *f* utilisée dans les calculs
d Niederschlagberechnungsgrund-
lage *f*

482 DESORPTION CURVE
curve of moisture content versus
soil moisture tension
f courbe *f* de désorption
d Desorptionskurve *f*

483 DESSICATION CRACK
crack due to shrinkage of a drying
volume (e.g. mud)
f joint *m* de dessiccation
d Trocknungsriss *m*

DETENTION, surface see 2714

484 DETENTIONS OF FLOW
f rétention *f* de l'écoulement
d Rückhaltung *f*

485 DETONATOR
small high powered primary explosive
charge used to set off main charge
f détonateur *m*
d Sprengkapsel *f*

DETRITAL ROCK, see clastic rock

486 DETRITUS
loose material originating from
disintegrated and weathered rock
f détritus *m*
d Schutt *m*; Detritus *m*

487 DEVIATION
deflection of a recording from a base
line such as shale line in SP logging
f déviation *f*
d Abweichung *f*

DEVIATION, mean see 2003

488 DEVONIAN
geologic period of the Paleozoic
era
f Dévonien *m*
d Devon *n*

489 DEWATER, TO
f drainer; dénoyer
d entwässern

490 DEWATERING
f drainage *m* d'eau; dénoyage *m*
d Entwässern *n*

491 DEW FORMATION
f formation *f* de rosée
d Taubildung *f*

492 DEW-POINT
point at which dew formation starts
for given temperature and humidity
conditions
f point *m* de rosée
d Taupunkt *m*

493 D-HORIZON
zone of bedrock in soil profile
f horizon *m* de la roche-mère
d Zone *f* des unverwitterten
   Ausgangsmaterials

494 DIAGENESIS
post depositional physical and
chemical changes in sediment
f diagénèse *f*
d Diagenese *f*; Gesteinsbildung *f*

DIAMETER, effective see 621
-, external see 696
-, inside see 1042
-, well see 2988

DIAMOND industrial see 1020

495 DIAMOND DRILLING
drilling method where diamond
studded bits are used
f forage *m* au diamant
d Diamantbohren *n*

496 DIAMOND DRILLING BIT
drilling bit studded with industrial
diamonds or containing diamond
fragments in an abrasive matrix
f trépan *m* au diamant
d Diamantbohrkrone *f*

497 DIASTROPHISM
epirogenetic and orogenetic
movements of the earth's crust

f diastrophisme *m*
d Diastrophismus *m*

498 DIATOMITE
powdered silica of diatomes
f diatomite *m*; terre *f* d'infusoires
d Diatomeenerde *f*; Infusorienerde *f*

499 DIELECTRIC CONSTANT
f constante *f* diélectrique
d Dielektrizitätskonstante *f*;
   dielektrische Konstante *f*

500 DIELECTRIC LOSS
f perte *f* diélectrique
d dielektrische Verschiebung *f*

501 DIFFERENTIAL PRESSURE
f pression *f* différentielle
d Druckunterschied *m*;
   Differentialdruck *m*

502 DIFFUSION
f diffusion *f*
d Diffusion *f*

DIFFUSION, molecular see 2067

503 DIFFUSION CONSTANT
f coefficient *m* de diffusion
d Diffusionskonstante *f*

DIFFUSION WELL, see recharge we

504 DIG, TO
action of mechanical excavation
of earth or rock other than drilling
f creuser
d ausschachten; graben

505 DIKE
wall or embankment protecting
lowlands from being flooded
f digue *f*
d Deich *m*

506 DIKE
sheet-like igneous rock intrusion
cutting across sediments
f filon *m*
d Gang *m*

507 DIMPLE SPRING
f source *f* ponctuelle
d Punktquelle *f*

508 DIOPSIDE
calcium silicate formed by contact
metamorphism
f diopside *m*
d Diopsid *m*

509 DIORITE
plutonic rock of crystalline
structure with predominantly light
and few basic components
f diorite *m*
d Diorit *m*

510 DIP
angle of inclination of a bed with
the horizontal at right angle to the
direction of strike
f pendage *m*
d Einfallen *n*

DIP, original see 2140

511 DIPMETER SURVEY
logging method where the dip of the
penetrated strata is measured
f pendagemétrie *f*
d Schichtneigungsmessung *f*

512 DIRECT CURRENT
f courant *m* direct
d Gleichstrom *m*

513 DIRECTIONAL DERIVATIVE
f dérivée *f* directionnelle
d richtungsgebundene Ableitung *f*

514 DIRECT RUNOFF;
DIRECT SURFACE RUNOFF;
STORM RUNOFF
runoff entering stream promptly
after rainfall
f ruissellement *m* de surface direct
d direkter Oberflächenabfluss *m*

515 DISCHARGE
volumetric flow of water through
a given cross section
f écoulement *m*; déchargement *m*
d Abfluss *m*; Ausfluss *m*; Durchfluss *m*

DISCHARGE, artificial see 116
-, evaporation see 678
-, groundwater see 900
-, hydraulic see 952
-, maximum see 1199
-, natural see 2098
-, pump see 2304
-, specific see 440

516 DISCHARGE, TO
action of fluid outflow or
throughflow
f débiter
d spenden; ausfliessen

517 DISCHARGE HYDROGRAPH
graph showing discharge of water
as a function of time
f hydrogramme *m* d'écoulement
d Abflussganglinie *f*;
Abflusshydrograph *m*

518 DISCHARGE PIPE
pipe through which a pump
discharges
f tuyau *m* de refoulement;
tuyau *m* de débit
d Druckrohr *n*

519 DISCHARGE PRESSURE
pressure at which a certain
discharge takes place
f pression *f* de refoulement
d Förderdruck *m*

520 DISCONFORMITY
geological unconformity between
parallel beds, often with some series
missing
f discontinuité *f*
d Diskordanz *f*

521 DISCONTINUITY
point where a mathematical function
becomes nondefined
f discontinuité *f*; singularité *f*;
d Diskontinuität *f*

522 DISCRETE VALUE
f valeur *f* discontinue
d diskrete Grösse *f*; diskontinuierlicher Wert *m*

523 DISPERSION
f dispersion *f*
d Verteilung *f*; Zerstreuung *f*;
Dispersion *f*

DISPERSION, hydrodynamic see 963

524 DISPERSION ZONE
zone of intermixing in miscible
flow or in sea water encroachment
f zone *f* de dispersion
d Dispersionszone *f*

525 DISPLACEMENT
process of replacing one fluid in
a porous medium by another
f déplacement *m*
d Verdrängung *f*

DISPLACEMENT, miscible,
see 2054

526 DISPLACEMENT PUMP
f pompe *f* foulante
d Verdrängungspumpe *f*

527 DISPOSAL WELL
injection well through which waste
water is disposed into the underground
f puits *m* d'injection; puits *m*
absorbant
d Schluckbohrung *f*;
Versenkbrunnen *m*

528 DISSOLVE, TO
f dissoudre
d auflösen

DISTRIBUTION, area elevation
see 106
-, frequency see 790
-, grain size see 865
-, random see 2334
-, saturation see 2471

529 DISTRIBUTION GRAPH
graph showing the frequency
distributions of the variates
f graphique *m* de distribution
d Verteilungskurve *f*

530 DISTURBANCE
in geology: any change of the
original position of rocks by folding
or faulting
f accident *m*
d Störung *f*

531 DISTURBED SAMPLE
sample disturbed with respect to
its original mode of packing and
sedimentation
f échantillon *m* perturbé
d gestörte Probe *f*

532 DITCH
shallow but long depression in the
ground surface
f fossé *m*
d Graben *m*

DITCH, drainage see 552

533 DITCH METHOD
water spreading method by ditches
f méthode *f* d'infiltration par
fossés
d Rieselgrabenverfahren *n*

534 DIURNAL
covering a period of 24 hours

f diurne
d täglich

535 DIVERT, TO
f déverser
d ableiten

536 DIVIDE
line connecting highest topographic
elevations that separate one
drainage basin from another
f ligne *f* de séparation (des eaux);
ligne *f* de partage
d Wasserscheide *f*; Scheide *f*

DIVIDE, drainage see 552
-, groundwater see 901, 902
-, topographic see 2800

537 DIVINING ROD
forklike branch or wire used in
water witching
f baguette *f* divinatoire
d Wünschelrute *f*

538 DOLINE
solution sinkhole in a karst region
f doline *f*
d Karsttrichter *m*; Doline *f*

539 DOLOMITE
rock composed mainly of dolomite
mineral Ca Mg $(CO_2)_2$
f dolomie *m*
d Dolomit *m*

540 DOUBLE ACTING PUMP
f pompe *f* à double effet
d doppelt wirkende Pumpe *f*

541 DOWNSTREAM
f en aval
d flussabwärts

542 DOWNWARPING
down bending of stratum to form a
depression or syncline
f ploiement *m* vers le bas
d Eindellung *f*; Einmuldung *f*

543 DOWSING;
WATER WITCHING
method of prospecting for water
with a divining rod
f hydromancie *f*
d Wünschelrutenmutung *f*;
Wassermutung *f* durch
Wünschelrutengänger

544 DRAG
resistance force of flowing fluid o

solid boundary
f résistance *f* à l'écoulement
   traînée *f*
d Strömungswiderstand *m*

545 DRAG BIT
rotary drilling bit
f outil *m* à lames
d Blattmeissel *m*

546 DRAG COEFFICIENT
f coefficient *m* de traînée
d Widerstandsbeiwert *m*

547 DRAIN
opening for a complete emptying
of a reservoir or container
f vidange *m*
d Ablass *m*

DRAIN, cleanout see 304

DRAINAGE, acid mine see 17
-, gravity see 882
-, internal see 1065
-, mine see 2045
-, roof see 2434

548 DRAINAGE AREA
horizontal projection of an area
drained by a particular river system
f aire *f* de drainage
d Abflussgebiet *n*; Einzugsgebiet *n*,
   Entwässerungsgebiet *n*

549 DRAINAGE BASIN
area contributing to runoff which
sustains streamflow
f bassin *m* versant
d Niederschlagsgebiet *n*

550 DRAINAGE DENSITY
ratio of total channel segments
lengths cumulated for all orders
to basin area
f densité *f* du réseau; densité *f*
   de drainage
d Flussdichte *f*

551 DRAINAGE DITCH
small channel through which
surface waters can drain off
f fossé *m* de drainage
d Entwässerungsgraben *m*

552 DRAINAGE DIVIDE
rim of a drainage basin
f ligne *f* de partage; ligne *f* de
   crête
d Wasserscheide *f*

553 DRAINAGE GALLERY
f galerie *f* de drainage
d Entwässerungsstollen *m*

554 DRAINAGE NETWORK
system of streams and rivers
draining a given basin
f réseau *m* de drainage;
   réseau *m* hydrographique
d Gewässernetz *n*;
   Abflussnetz *n*

555 DRAINAGE PATTERN
geometric arrangement of stream
segments in a drainage system
f configuration *f* de drainage
d Entwässerungsanordnung *f*

556 DRAINAGE RADIUS
radius of zone actually supplying
water to a pumping well
f rayon *m* d'appel
d Einzugsradius *m*

557 DRAINAGE RATIO
ratio of runoff to precipitation
f coefficient *m* de ruissellement;
   coefficient *m* d'écoulement
d Abflussfaktor *m*

558 DRAINAGE SYSTEM
network of streams and tributaries
f réseau *m* hydrographique;
   réseau *m* de drainage
d Entwässerungsnetz *n*

559 DRAIN TILE
porous pipe used for collection of
excess ground water
f tuyau *m* de drainage
d Dränagerohr *n*

560 DRAIN VALVE
f robinet *m* de vidange
d Ablasshahn *m*

561 DRAW
natural depression or small valley
f dépression *f* de la surface
d Delle *f*

562 DRAWDOWN
difference between the elevation of
initial piezometric surface and its
position after pumping
f rabattement *m*; baisse *f* du
   niveau dynamique
d Absenkung *f*; Absenkungsbetrag *m*

DRAWDOWN, residual see 2393
-, specific see 2616

563 DRAWDOWN CURVE
   plot of drawdown with radial
   distance from well
   f   courbe *f* rabattement-distance;
       courbe *f* de dépression
   d   Absenkungskurve *f*

564 DRAW WELL
   f   puits *m* à poulie
   d   Ziehbrunnen *m*

565 DRAW WORKS
   hoisting installation for the
   positioning and operation of drill
   pipe in a drilling rig
   f   treuil *m* de forage
   d   Hebewerk *n*

   DRIFT, glacial see 846

566 DRIFT SAND
   sand transported by wind action
   f   sable *m* éolien
   d   Treibsand *m*

567 DRILL
   f   trépan *m*
   d   Bohrer *m*

   DRILL, churn see 294

568 DRILL, TO
   action of bringing down a hole by
   cutting and removal of earth or rock
   material
   f   forer
   d   bohren

569 DRILL COLLAR
   heavy section of drill pipe above
   bit to give the necessary weight
   on the bit
   f   masse *f* tige
   d   Schwerstange *f*

570 DRILLER'S LOG
   log obtained through inspection of
   cuttings by driller
   f   diagraphie *f* du foreur
   d   Bohrprotokoll *n*

571 DRILLING
   penetration of rock formations
   with a drill
   f   forage *m*
   d   Bohren *n*

   DRILLING, air see 39
   -, cable see 216
   -, cable tool see 221

-, core see 392
-, deep well see 448
-, diamond see 495
-, exploration see 692
-, full hole see 799
-, percussion see 2194
-, shot see 2539

572 DRILLING BIT
   lower part of drill often replaceable
   in actual contact with the bottom
   hole where the rock face is disintegrated by chipping, abrasion, or
   scraping
   f   outil *m* à forage; trépan *m*
   d   Bohrmeissel *m*; Bohrkrone *f*

   DRILLING BIT, diamond see 496

573 DRILLING CABLE
   cable on which the drill string is
   suspended
   f   câble *m* de manoeuvre
   d   Bohrseil *n*

574 DRILLING CREW
   team of workers operating a drilling
   rig
   f   équipe *f* de foreurs
   d   Bohrmannschaft *f*

575 DRILLING FLUID
   general term for fluid circulating
   through drill pipe and annulus in
   order to carry drill cuttings to the
   surface; see also drilling mud
   f   fluide *m* de forage
   d   Bohrflüssigkeit *f*; Bohrspülung *f*

576 DRILLING FOREMAN
   f   chef *m* foreur
   d   Bohrmeister *m*

577 DRILLING HOOK
   hook to which swivelhead and drill-
   string is attached
   f   crochet *m* de forage
   d   Bohrhaken *m*

578 DRILLING LINE
   drilling cable
   f   câble *m* de forage
   d   Bohrseil *n*

579 DRILLING MUD
   drilling fluid with heavy solid
   suspension of mud base and drill
   cuttings, often thixotropic
   f   boue *f* de forage
   d   Bohrschlamm *m*; Bohrschmand

580   DRILLING RATE
      rate at which drilling progresses
      f   vitesse *f* de forage
      d   Bohrgeschwindigkeit *m*

581   DRILLING RIG
      a) frame structure over the drilling
         platform or, in a wider sense,
      b) the complete drilling installation
      f   a) mât de forage;
          b) installations *fpl* de forage
      d   a) Bohrturm *m*; Bohrgerüst *n*;
          b) Bohranlage *f*

582   DRILLING-TIME LOG
      log of drilling rate versus depth
      f   diagraphie *f* de l'avancement
      d   Bohrzeitprotokoll *n*

583   DRILL PIPE STRING
      length of all connected drill pipes
      f   train *m* de tiges
      d   Bohrstrang *m*

584   DRILL STEM
      string of connected drill pipe
      f   tiges *fpl* de forage
      d   Bohrgestänge *n*

585   DRILL STEM TEST (DST)
      open hole productivity test of a
      sealed off formation under pressure
      by way of the normally used drill stem
      f   essai *m* des couches par les tiges
          de forage; drill-stem-test *m*
      d   Gestängetest *m*; Drillstemtest *m*

586   DRINKING WATER
      f   eau *f* potable
      d   Trinkwasser *n*

587   DRIPSTONE
      rock formed by evaporation of
      dripping water film containing calcite
      f   colonne *f* de pierre formée
          par des concrétions calcaires
      d   Tropfstein *m*

588   DRIVE, TO
      action of making hole by desplace-
      ment of earth material
      f   enfoncer
      d   eintreiben

589   DRIVE CAP
      protective cap on upper end of
      pipe string receiving impacts
      from driving mechanism
      f   casque *m* de battage
      d   Treibkappe *f*

590   DRIVE CLAMP
      clamp transmitting impact to pipe

      in driving a well
      f   collier *m* de battage
      d   Treibschelle *f*

591   DRIVEN WELL
      well driven into loose sedimentary
      material by impacts of a driving
      mechanism
      f   puits *m* enfoncé
      d   gerammter Brunnen *m*;
          Schlagbrunnen *m*

592   DRIVE POINT;
      SAND POINT
      screened cylindrical pipe section
      with steel cone at bottom of pipe in
      well driven through unconsolidated
      formations
      f   cône *m* de sondage
      d   Treibspitze *f*; Rammspitze *f*;
          Bohrspitze *f*; Schlagbrunnenspitze *f*

593   DRIVER
      weight with which impact on pipe
      is created
      f   sonnette *f*
      d   Ramme *f*

594   DRIVING BAR
      f   colonne *f* de battage
      d   Treibstange *f*

595   DROP HAMMER
      f   mouton *m*
      d   Rammbär *m*

596   DROUGHT
      period of moisture deficiency and
      absence of water for plant growth
      f   sécheresse *f*
      d   Trockenheit *f*; Dürre *f*

597   DROWNED
      condition of underground openings
      such as caverns of mines that have
      been flooded
      f   inondé
      d   ersoffen

598   DRUM
      cylinder on which rope or cable
      is reeled in drilling operations;
      cylinder containing graph paper in
      recording operations
      f   tambour *m*
      d   Trommel *f*; Walze *f*

      DRUM, recording see 2365

599   DRUMLIN
      hill of glacial drift

f   drumlin *m*
d   Drumlin *m*; Rundhöcker *m*

600   DRY CELL
f   pile *f* sèche
d   Trockenbatterie *f*

601   DRY HOLE
hole not obtaining any production;
non-productive well
f   puits *m* sec
d   trockene *f* Bohrung;
   Fehlbohrung *f*

602   DRY ICE
CO_2 in solid form at $-78.5^\circ C$
f   glace *f* carbonique; neige *f*
   carbonique
d   Trockeneis *n*

603   DRYING OVEN
f   étuve *f*
d   Trockenofen *m*; Trockenschrank *m*

604   DRY RESIDUE
f   résidu *m* sec
d   Trockenrückstand *m*

605   DUG WELL
excavated well
f   puits *m* creusé
d   gegrabener Brunnen *m*;
   Schachtbrunnen *m*; Kessel-
   brunnen *m*

606   DULL BIT
f   outil *m* usé
d   stumpfer Meissel *m*

607   DUNE SAND
wind blown sand forming stable or
wandering dunes

f   sable *m* de dune
d   Dünensand *m*

608   DUPUIT'S ASSUMPTION
simplifying assumption for the
solution of a free surface well flow
problem
f   hypothèses *f pl* de Dupuit
d   Dupuit'sche Annahme *f*

609   DURATION CURVE
cumulative frequency curve of a
continuous time series (of
hydrologic parameters)
f   courbe *f* de durée;
   courbe *f* des débits classés
d   Dauerlinie *f*;
   Dauerkurve *f*

610   DUTY OF WATER
quantity of irrigation water needed
for crop maturing
f   demande *f* en eau d'irrigation
d   Bewässerungsbedarf *m*

611   DYNAMIC SIMILARITY
scaling procedure of model and
prototype where the relationship
of dynamic parameters is retained
f   similitude *f* dynamique
d   dynamische Ähnlichkeit *f*

612   DYNAMITE CHARGE
f   charge *f* de dynamite
d   Dynamitladung *f*

613   DYNAMOMETER
device measuring the momentum
force of stream velocity
f   dynamomètre *m*
d   Dynamomometer *n*; Kraftmesser
   Fliessdruckmesser *m*

E

614 EARTH CURRENT
natural telluric current present
in the earth's crust
f   courant *m* tellurique
d   Erdstrom *m*

615 EARTHFLOW
flow of water saturated earth
material in form of a mud stream
f   glissement *m* de terrain
d   Gleitfrana *f*

616 EARTHQUAKE
movement of the earth's crust due
to elastic waves originating from a
disturbance (epicenter)
f   séisme *m*; tremblement *m* de terre
d   Erdbeben *n*

617 EARTH TIDE
displacing effect of lunar attraction
on earth's crust
f   marée *f* terrestre
d   Erdgezeitenbewegung *f*

618 ECCENTRIC WELL
well not in center or circle of
influence
f   puits *m* excentrique
d   exzentrischer Brunnen *m*

619 EDDY
non laminar circulation of fluid at
boundaries of flow separation
f   tourbillon *m*
d   Wirbel *m*

EFFECT, bridging see 203
-, damping see 437
-, electrokinetic see 638
-, end see 647
-, skin see 2566

620 EFFECTIVE ABSTRACTIONS
difference between total precipitation
and effective precipitation
f   pertes *f pl* par absorption
d   effektive Rückhaltung *f*

621 EFFECTIVE DIAMETER
10 percentile size, i.e. 10 per cent
diameter smaller than this diameter
f   diamètre *m* effectif
d   wirksamer Korndurchmesser *m*

622 EFFECTIVE PERMEABILITY
f   perméabilité *f* effective
d   effektive Durchlässigkeit *f*

623 EFFECTIVE POROSITY;
PRACTICAL POROSITY
porosity concept only taking into
account the porespace that will
yield water under gravity; see
also specific yield
f   porosité *f* libre; capacité *f*
effective d'absorption
d   wirksame Porosität *f*

624 EFFECTIVE POROSITY
porosity concept only taking into
account interconnected pores
f   porosité *f* utile; porosité *f*
ouverte
d   effektive Porosität *f*

625 EFFECTIVE PRECIPITATION
part of precipitation contributing
entirely into direct runoff
f   précipitation *f* efficace
d   effektiver Niederschlag *m*

626 EFFECTIVE RAINFALL
effective precipitation when only
rainfall is involved
f   pluie *f* efficace
d   effektiver Regen *m*

EFFICIENCY, barometric see 141
-, temperature see 2753
-, tidal see 2784

627 EFFLUENT
outflow
f   effluent *m*
d   Ausfluss *m*

628 EFFLUENT STREAM;
GAINING STREAM
stream abstracting water from
ground water body, hence depleting
groundwater reserves
f   rivière *f* alimentée par la nappe
d   wasseraufnehmender Fluss *m*

629 EFFUSIVE ROCK
igneous rock produced by magmatic
material flowing out of or over the
earth's surface

f   roche *f* extrusive
d   Ergussgestein *n*

630   EFFUSION
extrusion of liquid igneous rock
on earth's surface
f   effusion *f*; épanchement *m*
d   Erguss *m*; Effusion *f*

631   ELASTIC PROPERTIES
properties describing deformation
of a solid
f   propriétés *f pl* élastiques
d   elastische Eigenschaften *f pl*

632   ELECTRICAL RESISTIVITY
f   résistivité *f* électrique
d   spezifischer elektrischer Widerstand *m*

633   ELECTRIC LOG
all well records obtained by
electrical (esp. resistivity) methods
f   carottage *m* électrique
d   elektrisches Kernen *n*

634   ELECTRO-CHEMICAL GAGING
flow measurement based on electric
detection of electrolyte tracer flow
f   jaugeage *m* chimique
d   Salzgeschwindigkeitsverfahren *n*

635   ELECTROCHEMICAL POTENTIAL
electrical potential due to differences
in ion concentrations of different
solutions in a bore hole environment
f   potentiel *f* électrochimique
d   elektrochemisches Potential *n*

ELECTRODE, current see 427
-, guard see 911
-, moving see 2082

636   ELECTRODE SPACING
distance between electrodes in
electric logging devices
f   espacement *m* des électrodes
d   Elektrodenabstand *m*

637   ELECTROFILTRATION
passage of filtrate through a
membrane under a voltage difference
f   électrofiltration *f*
d   Elektrofiltration *f*

638   ELECTROKINETIC EFFECT
motion of solids in suspension under
the influence of an electric field
f   effet *m* électrocinétique
d   elektrokinetischer Effekt *m*

639   ELECTROLYTE
f   électrolyte *m*
d   Elektrolyt *m*

640   ELEVATION
f   élévation *f*
d   Höhe *f*

ELEVATION DISTRIBUTION, area
see 106

641   ELEVATION HEAD
f   énergie *f* de position
d   Druckhöhe *f*

642   ELUTRIATION
washing process by decantation
with water
f   élutriation *f*
d   Aufschlämmen *n*

643   EMBANKMENT
natural or artificial lateral boundary
of a river
f   berge *f*
d   Ufer *n*; Uferböschung *f*

644   EMBOUCHURE
mouth of a river
f   embouchure *f*
d   Mündung *f*

645   EMULSION BREAKER
f   désémulsifiant *m*
d   Emulsionsspalter *m*

646   ENCROACHMENT
landward advancement of saline
waters into coastal aquifers;
displacement of clean water by
pollutants
f   envahissement *m*
d   Eindringen *n*; Vordringen *n*

647   END EFFECT
disturbance introduced by inflow
and outflow section in flow experime
f   effet *m* de bouts
d   Endeffekt *m*

648   ENDOGENIC
pertaining to geological process
originating within the earth
f   endogène
d   endogen; innenbürtig

ENERGY, free surface see 786

649   ENERGY BALANCE
f   bilan *m* énergétique
d   Energiebilanz *f*

650   ENERGY GRADE LINE
      f   ligne *f* de charge
      d   Energielinie *f*

651   ENERGY HEAD
      hydraulic head plus velocity head
      f   charge *f* totale
      d   Gesamthöhe *f* der Energielinie

652   ENERGY LINE
      f   ligne *f* de charge
      d   Energielinie *f*

653   ENERGY TRANSFER
      f   transfert *m* d'énergie
      d   Energieumsatz *m*

654   ENTHALPY
      heat content
      f   enthalpie *f*
      d   Wärmeinhalt *m*; Entalpie *f*

655   ENTRANCE CAPACITY
      property of soil to let water
      infiltrate; maximum value of this
      property
      f   capacité *f* de pénétration
      d   Eindringungskapazität *f*

656   ENTROPHY
      degree of thermodynamic disorder
      f   entrophie *f*
      d   Entropie *f*

657   EOCENE
      geologic epoch in the Tertiary
      period
      f   Eocène *m*
      d   Eozän *n*

658   EOLIAN DEPOSIT
      sediment material deposited by
      wind action
      f   dépôt *m* éolien
      d   Windablagerung *f*

659   EPHEMERAL STREAM
      stream flowing only in direct
      response to precipitation
      f   rivière *f* éphémère
      d   kurzfristig fliessender Fluss *m*

660   EPILIMNION
      upper layer of stratified water
      f   épilimnion *m*
      d   Epilimnion *n*

661   EPOCH
      subdivision of a period in the
      geologic time scale
      f   époque *f*
      d   Epoche *f*

EPOCH, glacial see 847

EQUATION, continuity
-, hydrologic see 976

662   EQUATION OF HYDROLOGIC
      EQUILIBRIUM
      mass balance for a ground water
      basin
      f   bilan *m* régional
      d   Gebietsbilanz *f*

663   EQUATION OF STATE
      f   équation *f* d'état
      d   Zustandsgleichung *f*

664   EQUIPOTENTIAL LINE
      line of equal potential
      f   équipotentielle *f*
      d   Linie *f* gleiches Potentials

EQUIVALENT, chemical see 286
-, moisture see 2065
-, water see 2934

665   EQUIVALENT PER MILLION (EPM)
      number of equivalent weights in a
      million parts per weight of solution
      f   équivalent *m* par million
      d   Äquivalenzgewicht *n* pro Million

666   ERA
      largest subdivision of the geologic
      time scale
      f   ère *f*
      d   Zeitalter *n*

667   ERODIBLE
      susceptible to erosion
      f   érodible
      d   erodierbar

668   EROSION
      sequence of processes of disintegration
      and transportation of rock material
      f   érosion *f*
      d   Erosion *f*; Abtragung *f*

EROSION, bank see 137
-, sheet see 2533

669   EROSIONAL PROCESS
      f   processus *m* d'érosion
      d   Erosionsvorgang *m*;
          Abtragungsvorgang *m*

670   EROSION SURFACE
      land surface resulting from the
      action of erosion
      f   surface *f* d'érosion
      d   Erosionsfläche *f*;
          Abtragungsfläche *f*

671 EROSIVENESS
capacity to erode
f pouvoir *m* érosif
d Erosionsfähigkeit *f*

672 ESCARPMENT
steep slope, often the result of
faulting
f escarpement *m*
d Steilabfall *m*; Stufe *f*

673 ESKER
stratified fluvio-glacial deposits
in form of ridges
f esker *m*
d Oser *m*; Wallberg *m*

674 ESTUARY
lower course of river discharging
into sea and subject to tidal currents
f estuaire *m*
d Mündung *f*

675 EUTROPHICATION
f eutrophication *f*
d Eutrophierung *f*

676 EVAPORATE
sedimentary rock formed by
evaporation and precipitation of
saline waters
f évaporit *m*
d Evaporit *m*; Saltzgestein *n*

677 EVAPORATION
change of water from liquid or solid
state into gaseous state through
heat exchange
f évaporation *f*
d Verdunstung *f*; Evaporation *f*

EVAPORATION, reservoir see 2391

678 EVAPORATION DISCHARGE
direct discharge of ground water
to atmosphere through evaporation
f débit *m* d'évaporation
d Bodenverdunstung *f*;
Wasserabgabe *f* durch Verdunstung

679 EVAPORATION LOSS
loss of precipitated water that is
discharged to atmosphere by
evaporation
f perte *f* par évaporation
d Verdunstungsverlust *m*

680 EVAPORATION OPPORTUNITY
amount of water made available for
discharge into atmosphere

f disponibilité *f* en eau (pour
l'évaporation)
d verfügbares Wasser *n* (für die
Verdunstung)

681 EVAPORATION PAN
open tank used to measure evaporation
f bac *m* évaporatoire
d Verdunstungskessel *m*

682 EVAPORATION REDUCTION
rate control of escape of water
vapor from an open surface
f réduction *f* de l'évaporation
d Verdunstungsverminderung *f*

683 EVAPORATION SUPPRESSION
complete prevention of evaporation
by mechanical or physico-chemical
means (e.g. monomolecular layer)
f suppression *f* de l'évaporation
d Verdunstungsunterdrückung *f*

684 EVAPORATIVITY
evaporative power
f pouvoir *m* évaporant
d Verdunstungsvermögen *n*

685 EVAPORITE ROCKS
f roche *f* hydatogène
d Eindampfungsgestein *n*;
Salzgestein *n*

686 EVAPOTRANSPIRATION
return of water in vapor form to
atmosphere through combined action
of evaporation, plant transpiration
and sublimation
f évapotranspiration *f*
d Evapotranspiration *f*;
Gesamtverdunstung *f*

EVAPOTRANSPIRATION,
potential see 2279

687 EXCAVATE, TO
f creuser
d graben; ausgraben

EXCHANGE, gas see 815
-, heat see 925

688 EXCHANGE CAPACITY
f pouvoir *m* d'échange ionique
d Austauschvermögen *n*;
Austauschfähigkeit *f*

689 EXOGENIC
pertaining to processes on or near
the surface of the earth

f   exogène
d   exogen; aussenbürtig

690 EXPANSION JOINT
f   joint *m* d'expansion
d   Ausdehnungsverbindung *f*

691 EXPERIMENTAL BASIN
basin chosen for the thorough
study of hydrological phenomenon
f   bassin *m* échantillon
d   Beobachtungsgebiet *n*;
Versuchsbecken *n*

EXPLORATION, geophysical
see 839

692 EXPLORATION DRILLING
drilling for the purpose of subsurface
geological reconnaissance
f   forage *m* de reconnaissance
d   Schürfbohrung *f*; Aufschluss-
bohrung *f*

693 EXPLOSION
f   explosion *f*
d   Sprengung *f*; Explosion *f*

694 EXPLOSIVE
f   explosif *m*
d   Sprengstoff *m*

695 EXPOSURE SITE
f   endroit *m* exposé
d   Messtelle *f*

696 EXTERNAL DIAMETER
f   diamètre *m* extérieur
d   Aussendurchmesser *m*

697 EXTERNAL LOADS
external loads causing water level
fluctuation in well
f   charge *f* extérieure; charge *f*
accidentelle
d   externe Belastung *f*; Fremdbelastung *f*

698 EXTRUSIVE ROCK
see effusive rock
f   roche *f* extrusive
d   Extrusivgestein *n*; Ergussgestein *n*

F

699 **FACIES**
lithologic appearance of a rock
f faciès *m*
d Fazies *f*

700 **FACIES CHANGE**
f changement *m* de faciès
d Fazieswechsel *m*

FACTOR, climatic see 307
-, conversion see 381
-, deposition see 466
-, form see 780
-, formation see 776
-, formation-resistivity see 778
-, leakage see 1145
-, lithologic see 1156
-, scaling see 2479
-, structural see 2678
-, weighing see 2977
-, wind see 3017

701 **FAILING WELL**
well yielding less water with time
f puits *m* tarissant
d versiegender Brunnen *m*

702 **FALL**
gross slope of a river
f chute *f*; pente *f*
d Reliefenergie *f*; Gefäll *n*

703 **FAMILY OF CURVES**
f famille *f* de courbes
d Kurvenschaar *f*

FAN, alluvial see 58
-, talus see 2747

704 **FAN SHOOTING**
method of arranging shot holes in
a seismic survey
f tir *m* en éventail
d Fächerschiessen *n*

705 **FATHOMETER**
water depth measuring device
f sondeur *m* de la profondeur d'eau
d Wassertiefenmessgerät *n*

706 **FAULT**
fracture of a rock mass along which
dislocation has taken place
f faille *f*
d Verwerfung *f*; Sprung *m*

FAULT, cross see 416
-, longitudinal see 1168
-, normal see 2115
-, reverse see 2406

707 **FAULT LINE**
intersection of the fault with the
surface of the earth or any other
plane of reference
f ligne *f* de faille
d Verwerfungslinie *f*

708 **FAULT PLANE**
plane on which dislocation and
relative movement has taken place
f plan *m* de faille
d Verwerfungsebene *f*

709 **FAULT SCARP**
elevation formed by movement of
blocks along a fault plane
f escarpement *m* de faille
d Bruchstufe *f*; Verwerfungsstufe

710 **FAULT ZONE**
zone with numerous small parallel
faults
f zone *f* failleuse
d Verwerfungszone *f*; Störungszone

711 **FEEDING DEVICE**
f doseur *m*
d Dosiergerät *n*

712 **FELDSPAR**
very common group of rock forming
minerals
f feldspath *m*
d Feldspat *m*

713 **FERRIC OXIDE**
Fe_2O_3, rust, hematite
f oxyde *m* ferrique
d Eisenoxyd *n*; Eisenrost *m*

714 **FERRITO ZONE**
zone of iron oxide accumulation in
soil under humid climate
f horizon *m* ferrugineux; alios *m*
ferrugineux
d eisenhaltige Ausfällungszone *f*

715 **FERRUGINOUS**
f ferrugineux
d eisenhaltig

FIELD, vector see 2886
-, well see 2998
-, wind see 3018

716 FIELD CAPACITY;
     FIELD-CARRYING CAPACITY;
     CAPILLARY CAPACITY
     soil moisture retained by capillarity,
     not removable by gravity drainage;
     specific retention
     f capacité *f* au champ, capacité *f*
        capillaire
     d Feldkapazität *f*

717 FIELD COEFFICIENT OF
     PERMEABILITY
     defined for field temperature
     conditions in gpd/ft^2 under a unit
     gradient
     f coefficient *m* de perméabilité
        Darcy sur le terrain
     d Feldwert *m* der Durchlässig-
        keitsziffer

718 FIELD SURVEY
     measurements taken in the field
     f étude *f* sur terrain
     d Felduntersuchung *f*

719 FIELD TEST
     test run in the field under normal
     field conditions
     f essai *m* sur le terrain
     d Feldversuch *m*

720 FIELD VELOCITY OF GROUND
     WATER
     actual interstitial velocity
     f vitesse *f* de terrain
     d tatsächliche Grundwasserfliess-
        geschwindigkeit *f*
        Abstandsgeschwindigkeit *f*

721 FIELD WORK
     f travaux *mpl* de terrain
     d Feldarbiet *m*

     FILL, gravel see 872
     -, valley see 2878

722 FILL TERRACE
     elevated valley surface formed by
     aggregation
     f terrasse *f* de remblaiement;
        terrasse *f* d'accumulation
     d Aufschüttungsterrasse *f*;
        Aufschotterungsterrasse *f*

723 FILTER
     screen through which water enters
     a well
     f filtre *m*
     d Filter *m*

724 FILTER CAKE
     cake of solid residue left on filter
     f cake *m* de boue; gâteau *m* de
        boue; dépôt *m* de filtration
     d Filterkuchen *m*

725 FILTER PLANT
     f installation *f* de filtration
     d Filteranlage *f*

     FILTRATION SPRING
     see seepage spring

726 FINE GRAINED SAND
     f sable *m* fin
     d Feinsand *m*

727 FINE GRAVEL
     rock aggregates of 2 - 1 mm
     diameter (USBS)
     f sable *m* très gros
     d feiner Kies *m*

728 FINE SAND
     grain diameter 0.25 to 0.1 mm
     (USBS)
     f sable *m* fin
     d Feinsand *m*

729 FINITE DIFFERENCES METHOD
     method of solution for partial
     differential equations
     f méthode *f* par différences finies
     d Methode *f* der endlichen
        Differenzen

730 FIRN
     compacted granular snow
     f névé *m*
     d Firn *m*

731 FISHING TOOL
     device for the retrieval of broken
     or stuck drilling tools
     f outil *m* de repêchage
     d Fangwerkzeug *n*

732 FISHTAIL
     drilling bit with fish tail like double
     winged cutting edges
     f outil *m* bilame
     d Fischschwanzmeissel *m*

733 FISSURE
     open joint or crack in rocks
     f fissure *f*; crevasse *f*
     d Spalte *f*

734 FIXED BOUNDARY
     f limite *f* fixe
     d festgelegte Grenze *f*

735 FLANK
limb of a fold
f flanc *m*
d Flanke *f*; Schenkel *m*

736 FLASH FLOOD
relatively short but very intense
flood
f torrent *m*
d Sturzflut *f*

737 FLEXIBLE HOSE
f flexible *m*; tuyeau *m* flexible
d Schlauch *m*; biegsamer Schlauch *m*

738 FLEXURE
bend in stratum with one flank or
limb only
f flexure *f*
d Flexur *f*

739 FLOAT
f flotteur *m*
d Schwimmer *m*

740 FLOAT GAGE
device indicating or recording
water level with a float
f limnigraphe *m* à flotteur;
niveau *m* à flotteur
d Schwimmerschreibpegel *m*;
Flüssigkeitsstandanzeiger *m* mit
Schwimmer

741 FLOATING PAN
evaporation pan floating in water
body with drum floats
f bac *m* flottant
d Flossverdunstungskessel *m*

742 FLOCCULATION
f floculation *f*
d Ausflockung *f*; Ausfällung *f*

743 FLOOD
high river flow overtopping banks
f inondation *f*; crue *f*
d Überschwemmung *f*; Hochwasser *n*; Ausuferung *f*

FLOOD, design see 480
-, flash see 736

744 FLOOD-CONTROL
all measures to prevent or
diminish the effects of flooding
f protection *f* contre les crues
d Hochwasserschutz *m*

745 FLOOD CREST
peak of flood wave

f pointe *f* de crue
d Hochwasserscheitel *m*

746 FLOODING METHOD
recharge method by flooding
recharge area
f méthode *f* d'infiltration par
inondation
d Überschwemmungsmethode *f*

747 FLOODMARKS
marks left on fixed objects by
flood waters
f délaissés *mpl* de crue
d Hochwasserspuren *fpl*

748 FLOOD PLAIN
area of overbank flow
f zone *f* inondable; plaine *f*
d'inondation
d Überschwemmungsgebiet *n*;
Ausuferungsgebiet *n*

749 FLOOD PROFILE
continuous line representing the
water surface for a given rate of
flow
f profil *m* de crue
d Hochwasserlängsschnitt *m*

750 FLOOD ROUTING
f propagation *f* de crues
d Hochwasserweiterleitung *f*

751 FLOOD WATER
f eau *fpl* en crue
d steigendes Wasser *n*

752 FLOOD WAVE
f onde *f* de crue
d Flutwelle *f*

753 FLOTATION
f flottation *f*
d Flotieren *n*

FLOW, overland see 2159
-, potential see 2280
-, pyroclastic see 2314
-, radial see 2321
-, rapid see 2337
-, recession see 2355
-, return see 2404
-, saturated see 2469
-, sheet see 2534
-, steady see 2644
-, stream see 2666
-, subsurface see 2689, 2690
-, subsurface storm see 2690
-, tranquil see 2816
-, unconfined see 2858
-, uniform see 2866
-, unsaturated see 2870
-, unsteady see 2871
-, virgin see 2895

754 FLOW, TO
     f couler
     d fliessen

755 FLOW DURATION CURVE
     curve of cumulative streamflow
     versus corresponding per cent of
     time
     f courbe f de durée des débits
     d Dauerlinie f der Abflussmenge

756 FLOWING ARTESIAN WELL
     well with piezometric surface
     above ground surface
     f source f artésienne en libre
        débit
     d frei fliessender artesischer
        Brunnen m

757 FLOWING PRESSURE
     f pression f en débit
     d Fliessdruck m

758 FLOW-MASS CURVE
     mass curve with runoff discharge
     as hydrologic quantity; integral
     curve of hydrograph
     f courbe f du débit cumulé
     d Summenganglinie f

759 FLOWMETER
     instrument to measure volumetric
     flowrate
     f débimètre m
     d Durchflussmessgerät n

     FLOWMETER, mass see 1193
     -, volumetric see 2908

760 FLOW NET
     net of orthogonal streamlines

and equipotential lines applied in
the graphical solution of Laplace's
equation
     f réseau m orthogonal des lignes
        de courant et des courbes
        isopièzes
     d Strömungsnetz n;
        Strom-und Potentialliniennetz n

761 FLOW RATE
     volumetric rate of flow
     f débit m
     d Fliessrate f; Spende f

762 FLOW REGIMEN
     systematic behavior of a flow
     system as controlled by gravity,
     viscous or intomolecular forces
     (i.e. turbulent regimen)
     f régime m
     d Regime n

763 FLOW RESISTANCE
     f résistance f à l'écoulement
     d Fliesswiderstand m

764 FLOWTEST
     f essai m d'écoulement
     d Fliesstest m

765 FLOW WITH WATER TABLE
     unconfined flow
     f écoulement m en nappe phréatique
     d Grundwasserfluss m mit freier
        Oberfläche

766 FLUID
     f fluide m
     d Flüssigkeit f

     FLUID, drilling see 576
     -, homogeneous see 942

767 FLUID-VELOCITY LOG
     vertical record of fluid velocities
     in a well bore
     f diagraphie f de la vitesse
        d'écoulement
     d Fliessgeschwindigkeitslog n

768 FLUME
     channel supported on or above ground
     f rigole f
     d Gerinne n; Rinne f

     FLUME, critical depth see 411
     -, measuring see 2010

769 FLUORESCEIN
     f florescéine f
     d Fluoreszein n

770 FLUORITE
fluorspar, CaF_2
f fluorine *f*
d Flusspat *m*

771 FLUSHED ZONE
in electric logging practice the
zone around the well bore completely
invaded by the mud filtrate
f zone *f* envahie
d geflutete Zone *f*

772 FLUX
volume flow per unit area in unit
time
f flux *m*
d spezifischer Fluss *m*

773 FOLD
bend in stratum with two flanks,
often in anticlinal and synclinal
sequence
f pli *m*
d Falte *f*

774 FOOT VALVE
f clapet *m* de fond
d Bodenventil *n*

FORCE, body see 189
-, capillary see 238
-, gravity see 883
-, osmotic see 2144
-, viscous see 2898

775 FORCE POTENTIAL
f potentiel *m* de force
d Kraftpotential *n*

FORMATION, dew see 491
-, lacustrine see 1117
-, multiaquifer see 2093
-, rock see 2429

776 FORMATION FACTOR
ratio of bulk resistivity of
saturated sample to resistivity of
saturating solution
f facteur *m* de formation
d Formationsfaktor *m*

777 FORMATION OF RAIN
f formation *f* de pluie
d Regenbildung *f*

778 FORMATION-RESISTIVITY FACTOR
see formation factor
f facteur *m* de formation
d Formationswiderstandsfaktor *m*

779 FORMATION TEMPERATURE
temperature prevailing in a given
subsurface formation
f température *f* de formation
d Formationstemperatur *f*

780 FORM FACTOR
factor indicating shape and form of
mineral aggregates influencing their
hydrodynamic properties
f facteur *m* de forme
d Formfaktor *m*

781 FOUNTAIN
free flowing well or spring
f fontaine *f*
d Springbrunnen *m*; Quelle *f*

782 FRACTURE
breakage of rock strata
f fracture *f*
d Bruch *m*

783 FRACTURE SPRING
spring with outflow openings
consisting of fractures
f source *f* de fissures
d Kluftquelle *f*

784 FRACTURING
formation of breaks in a rock due
to folding or faulting
f fracturation *f*
d Bruchbildung *f*

FRACTURING, hydraulic see 953
-, well see 2990

785 FRAME
superstructure containing working
parts in drilling rig assembly
f monture *f*
d Gestell *n*; Rahmen *m*

786 FREE SURFACE ENERGY
f énergie *f* libre de surface
d freie Oberflächenenergie *f*

787 FREEZING POINT
point at which a liquid solidifies
f point *m* de congélation
d Gefrierpunkt *m*

788 FREQUENCY
number of occurrences of a varia
f fréquence *f*
d Frequenz *f*; Häufigkeit *f*

FREQUENCY, stream see 2667

789   FREQUENCY ANALYSIS
      f   analyse *f* fréquentielle
      d   Frequenzanalyse *f*;
          Häufigkeitsanalyse *f*

790   FREQUENCY DISTRIBUTION
      distribution of the number of
      occurrences of a variate
      f   distribution *f* de fréquence
      d   Häufigkeitsverteilung *f*

791   FRESH WATER
      water containing from 0 to 1000 ppm
      total dissolved solids
      f   eau *f* douce
      d   Frischwasser *n*; Süsswasser *n*

792   FRESH-WATER BARRIER
      barrier of fresh water injected to
      stop inflow of sea water into coastal
      aquifer
      f   barrage *m* souterrain en eau
          douce
      d   Süsswasserbarriere *f*

793   FRESH WATER LENS
      lenticular form of fresh water body
      under oceanic islands
      f   lentille *f* d'eau douce
      d   Frischwasserlinse *f*

794   FRIABLE
      f   friable; fragile
      d   brüchig; mulmig

795   FRICTION COEFFICIENT
      f   coefficient *m* de frottement
      d   Reibungsbeiwert *m*

796   FRICTION HEAD
      head loss due to energy
      dissipation by friction
      f   perte *f* de charge
      d   Reibungsverlust *m*

797   FRONT RANGE
      the outer part of a mountain
      range rising above the plain
      f   avant-montagne *f*
      d   Vorgebirge *n*

798   FROST IN THE SOIL
      f   gel *m* dans le sol
      d   Bodenfrost *m*

      FROST ZONE, annual see 84

799   FULL HOLE DRILLING
      drilling method where total cross
      section of hole is removed (as
      opposed to core drilling)
      f   forage *m* plein diamètre
      d   Vollbohrverfahren *n*

800   FUMAROLE
      volcanic exhalation of gases,
      mainly water vapor
      f   fumerolle *f*
      d   Fumarole *f*

801   FUNICULAR REGIME
      distribution of continuous liquid phase
      along pore walls with gaseous phase at
      pore center
      f   régime *m* d'eau funiculaire
      d   funikuläres Wasser *n*;
          zusammenhängendes Oberflächen-
          haftwasser *n*

G

802 **GABBRO**
dark alkaline plutonic rock with very
low feldspar content
f gabbro *m*
d Gabbro *m*

GAGE, Bourdon see 198
-, bubble see 206
-, chain see 275
-, float see 740
-, hook see 943
-, mercury see 2027
-, natural see 2099
-, nonrecording see 2112
-, precipitation see 2288
-, rain see 2331
-, recording see 2366
-, snow see 2582
-, staff see 2630
-, storage see 2652
-, tape see 2748
-, wire see 3019

803 **GAGE FLOW**
f débit *m* jaugé
d Eichfluss *m*

804 **GAGE PRESSURE**
normally pressure above atmospheric, absolute pressure minus
reference pressure
f surpression *f* atmosphérique
d Atmosphärenüberdruck *m*

805 **GAGE TANK**
tank used for volume measurements
f bac *m* de jaugeage; réservoir-
jaugeur *m*
d Messtank *m*

806 **GAGE WELL**
stilling well in which stage
measurements are performed
f puits *m* de limnigraphe
puits *m* de mesure
d Schwimmerschacht *m*;
Messchacht *m*

807 **GAGE ZERO**
f zéro *m* de l'échelle
d Skalennullpunkt *m*; Pegelnull-
punkt *m*

GAGING, electro-chemical
see 634
-, water see 2935

808 **GAGING STATION**
point at which stage measurements
are performed
f station *f* de jaugeage
d Messtation *f*; Messwarte *f*

GAINING STREAM
see effluent stream

809 **GALVANOMETER**
sensitive current meter
f galvanomètre *m*
d Galvanometer *n*

810 **GAMMA LOG**
vertical record of gamma-ray
measurements in a well
f diagraphie *f* de rayons gamma
d Gammalog *n*

811 **GARNET**
accessory mineral in igneous and
metamorphic rocks
f grenat *m*
d Granat *m*

812 **GAS**
f gaz *m*
d Gas *n*

813 **GAS BEARING**
containing gas
f gazéifère
d gasführend

814 **GAS CUSHION**
irretrievable gas pumped into an
aquifer to form reservoir space for
the storage of natural gas
f matelas *m* de gaz
d Gaspolster *n*

815 **GAS EXCHANGE**
f échange *m* de gaz
d Gasaustausch *m*

816 **GAS EXPANSION METHOD**
measurement of porosity based on
Boyle-Mariotte's gas laws
f méthode *f* par expansion de gaz;
méthode *f* par compression
(Mariotte)
d Gasausdehnungsmehtode *f*
(Boyle-Mariotte)

817 GAS EXTRACTION
     f dégazage *m*
     d Entgasung *f*

818 GASKET
     f étanchéité *f*; joint *m*;
        garniture *f*
     d Dichtung *f*

819 GAS PIPE LINE
     f gazoduc *m*
     d Gasleitung *f*; Gasfernleitung *f*

820 GAS SATURATION
     f saturation en gaz *f*
     d Gassättigung *f*

821 GAS TRAP
     f séparateur de gaz *m*
     d Gasabscheider *m*

     GATE, main see 1183

822 GATE VALVE
     f vanne *f* principale
     d Schieber *m*; Hauptschieber *m*

823 GEAR PUMP
     f pompe *f* à engrenage
     d Zahnradpumpe *f*; Getriebepumpe *f*

824 GEOCHEMISTRY
     science of the qualitative and
     quantitative identification of the
     elements and their distribution in
     the earth
     f géochimie *f*
     d Geochemie *f*

825 GEODESY
     science of measuring the geometrical
     properties of the earth
     f géodésie *f*
     d Geodäsie *f*; Vermessungskunde *f*

826 GEOHYDROLOGIC UNIT
     combination of aquifers and
     confining beds in a distinct
     hydrologic system
     f groupe *m* géohydrologique
     d geohydrologische Einheit *f*

827 GEOHYDROLOGY
     branch of hydrology relating to
     quantitative treatment of ground-
     water occurrence and flow
     f géohydrologie *f*; hydrologie *f*
        des nappes souterraines
     d Geohydrologie *f*; Hydrologie *f*
        des Grundwassers

828 GEOLOGICAL COLUMN
     vertical cross section through a
     sequence of formations
     f coupe *f* lithologique
     d Schichtprofil *n*

829 GEOLOGICAL SECTION
     vertical section through a sequence
     of rock masses or strata
     f coupe *f* géologique
     d geologischer Schnitt *m*

830 GEOLOGIC CONDITIONS
     f conditions *fpl* géologiques
     d geologische Verhältnisse *npl*

831 GEOLOGIC CONTROL
     influence of geologic factors on
     hydrogeologic features
     f facteur *m* d'influence hydrogéolo-
        gique
     d geologische Beeinflussung *f*;
        hydrologischer Parameter *m*

832 GEOLOGIC CORRELATION
     correlation of geologic formations
     as shown in logs over a given area
     f corrélation *f* géologique
     d geologische Korrelation *f*

833 GEOLOGIC LOG
     vertical cross section of the
     lithologic column indicating geologic
     and petrographic data
     f diagraphie *f* géologique;
        coupe *f* lithologique
     d geologisches Log *n*

834 GEOMETRIC MEAN
     f moyenne *f* géométrique
     d geometrisches Mittel *n*

835 GEOMETRIC SIMILARITY
     model-prototype length ratio
     f similitude *f* géométrique
     d geometrische Ähnlichkeit *f*

836 GEOMORPHIC PROCESS
     process responsible for the
     formation and alteration of the
     earth's surface
     f procédé *m* géomorphique
     d landschaftsformender Vorgang *m*

837 GEOMORPHOLOGY
     science of the origin and evolution
     of land forms
     f géomorphologie *f*
     d Geomorphologie *f*

838 GEOPHONE
instrument to pick up seismic
signals in the audio frequency
range
f sismomètre *m*
d Geophon *n*

839 GEOPHYSICAL EXPLORATION
exploration of subsurface features
by indirect or geophysical methods
f exploration *f* géophysique
d geophysikalische Exploration *f*

840 GEOPHYSICS
science of the physical properties
of the earth
f géophysique *f*
d Geophysik *f*

841 GEOTHERMAL
f géothermique
d geothermisch

842 GEOTHERMAL GRADIENT
increase of temperature with depth
(1°C per 100 ft.)
f gradient *m* géothermique
d geothermischer Gradient *m*

843 GEYSER
intermittent thermal spring
f source *f* geysérienne; geyser *m*
d Geysir *m*; Springquelle *f*

844 GHYBEN-HERZBERG CONDITIONS
equilibrium condition at interface
of immiscible fresh-water bodies
and salt-water bodies in coastal
aquifers
f conditions *f pl* de Ghyben-Herzberg
d Ghyben-Herzberg'sche
Bedingungen *f pl*

845 GLACIAL DEPOSIT
sedimentary deposits due to
transport in glaciers
f dépôt *m* glaciaire
d Glazialablagerung *f*

846 GLACIAL DRIFT
sediment material contained, transported and deposited by glaciers
f éboulis *m* glaciaire
d Gletscherschutt *m*

847 GLACIAL EPOCH
time in earth's history during which
extensive glaciation occurred
f période *f* glaciaire
d Eiszeit *f*

848 GLACIAL GROOVE
groove cut into bedrock by rock
fragments at the bottom of a moving
glacier
f cannelure *f* glaciaire
d Gletscherfurche *f*

849 GLACIAL TILL
drift material directly deposited
by ice
f argile *f* à blocaux
d Geschiebemergel *m*

850 GLACIATION
covering of land surface by glacier
ice
f glaciation *f*
d Vergletscherung *f*

851 GLACIER
extensive body of ice covering the
land surface
f glacier *m*
d Gletscher *m*

GLACIER, active see 21

852 GLACIER MILK
white colored melt water issued
from glacier
f lait *m* de glacier
d Gletschermilch *f*

853 GLACIER TONGUE
f lobe *m* du glacier
d Gletscherzunge *f*

854 GLACIOLOGY
science concerned with the
formation and action of ice
accumulations on the earth
f glaciologie *f*
d Glaziologie *f*

855 GNEISS
highly metamorphic rock of about
same mineral composition as grani
f gneiss *m*
d Gneiss *m*

856 GOOSE NECK
f col *m* de cygne
d Spülkopfkrümmer *m*

857 GORGE
narrow passage or canyon in a
mountain system
f gorge *f*
d Schlucht *f*

858 GRABEN
depression formed by a fault block
moving downward on the two
bounding faults
f bloc *m* affaissé
d Graben *m*; Tiefscholle *f*

859 GRADATION
leveling of a surface to a common
level
f aplanissement *m*; nivellement *m*
d Einebnung *f*

GRADATION, lateral see 1133

860 GRADE
inclination, slope
f degré *m*
d Steigung *f*; Neigung *f*

861 GRADIENT
maximum value of the directional
derivative
f gradient *m*
d Gradient *m*

GRADIENT, geothermal see 842
-, hydraulic see 954

862 GRAIN PACKING
spatial arrangement of grains forming
porous medium
f arrangement *m* des grains;
   tassement *m* des grains
d Kornpackung *f*

GRAINS, well sorted see 3000

863 GRAIN SHAPE
geometrical aspect of grain
f forme *f* d'une particule
d Korngestalt *f*

864 GRAIN SIZE
f taille *f* des grains
d Korngrösse *f*

865 GRAIN SIZE DISTRIBUTION
f distribution *f* granulométrique
d Korngrössenverteilung *f*

866 GRANODIORITE
acid plutonic rock
f granodiorite *m*
d Granodiorit *m*

867 GRANULAR
of structure clearly showing grain
shape
f granuleux
d körnig

868 GRANULE
small rounded grain or rock fragment
f granule *f*
d Körnchen *n*; Korn *n*

869 GRAPNEL
f grappin *m*
d Glückshaken *m*; Fanghaken *m*

870 GRAVEL
waterworn rounded rock grains
and fragments
f gravier *m*
d Kies *m*

GRAVEL, crushed see 419
-, fine see 727
-, outwash see 2150

871 GRAVEL ENVELOPE
gravel fill introduced around filter
screen in a well
f enveloppe *f* de gravier
d Kiesmantel *m*

872 GRAVEL FILL
f remblai *m* de gravier
d Schotterfüllung *f*

873 GRAVEL PACKING
gravel envelope surrounding
perforated casing in a well
f filtre *m* de gravier
d Kiesschüttung *f*

874 GRAVEL PIT
f gravière *f*
d Kiesgrube *f*

875 GRAVEL WALL
gravel packing around screened
well to increase effective diameter
f filtre *m* de gravier
d Kiesfilter *m*

876 GRAVIMETER
instrument to measure gravity,
especially gravity anomalies
f gravimètre *m*
d Gravimeter *n*; Schweremesser *m*

877 GRAVIMETRIC MOISTURE CONTENT
ratio of water weight to weight of
solid particles
f teneur *f* en humidité par
   gravimétrie
d gravimetrischer Feuchtegehalt *m*

878 GRAVITATIONAL WATER
water that can be drained by gravity

f   eau *f* de gravité; eau *f*
   gravifique
d   Schwerewasser *n*

GRAVITY, specific see 2618

879   GRAVITY ACCELERATION
f   accélération *f* de la pesanteur
d   Erdbeschleunigung *f*

880   GRAVITY ANOMALY
discrepancy between theoretically
expected and actually measured
gravity
f   anomalie *f* de la gravité
d   Schwereanomalie *f*

881   GRAVITY COMPONENT
component acting in the direction
of gravitation
f   composante *f* de gravitation
d   Schwerekomponente *f*

882   GRAVITY DRAINAGE
flow of water towards a well under
its own weight
f   drainage *m* par gravité
d   Schwerkraftentwässerung *f*

883   GRAVITY FORCE
f   force *f* de gravité
d   Schwerkraft *f*

884   GRAVITY METHOD
geophysical method of measuring
density differences of geological
structures
f   méthode *f* gravimétrique
d   Schweremessmethode *f*

885   GRAVITY SPRING
spring flowing under gravity
f   source *f* de déversement
d   Auslaufquelle *f*

886   GRAYWACKE
metamorphosed sandstone with
high feldspar content
f   grauwacke *m*
d   Grauwacke *f*

887   GREENSAND
sand containing glauconite
f   sable *m* vert
d   Grünsand *m*

GROUND ICE, see anchor ice

888   GROUNDING
f   mise *f* à la terre
d   Erdung *f*

889   GROUND LEVEL
f   niveau *m* du sol
d   Geländeoberfläche *f*

890   GROUND SLOPE
inclination of the ground surface
with the horizontal
f   inclinaison *f* du terrain
d   Geländeneigung *f*

891   GROUND TERMINAL
terminal connecting an electrical
system to the ground
f   mise *f* à la terre; borne *f* de
   mise à la terre
d   Erdungsanschluss *m*

892   GROUND WATER;
   PHREATIC WATER
that part of the underground or subsurface water that is contained in the
zone of saturation. Its lower limits
are the zone of rock flowage or the
lower confining bed, its upper limits
are the upper confining bed or the
water table
f   eaux *f pl* souterraines; eau *f*
   phréatique
d   Grundwasser *n*

GROUND WATER, native see 2097
-, perched see 2190

893   GROUNDWATER ARTERY
tubular body of permeable water-
filled material surounded by confin-
beds
f   veine *f* d'eau
d   Grundwasserader *f*

894   GROUNDWATER BARRIER
see groundwater dam
f   barrière *f* naturelle dans un
   aquifère; barrage *m* souterrain
d   Grundwasserbarriere *f*

895   GROUNDWATER BASIN
area throughout which groundwater
drains towards the same point; can
be larger than drainage basin if
permeable layers extend outside o
topographic divide
f   bassin *m* hydrogéologique
d   Grundwasserbecken *n*;
   Grundwassereinzugsgebiet *n*

896   GROUNDWATER CAPTURE
f   captage *m* des eaux souterraine
d   Grundwassererschliessung *f*

897 GROUNDWATER CASCADE
     flow of groundwater over a sub-
     surface barrier
     f cascade *f* souterraine
     d Grundwasserüberfall *m*

898 GROUNDWATER CEMENT
     cementing material precipitating at
     the water table
     f ciment *m* illuvial
     d Grundwasserzement *m*;
        Ausfällungszement *m*

899 GROUNDWATER DAM
     geological stratum serving as a
     subsurface dam
     f barrage *m* souterrain naturel,
        seuil *m* hydraulique;
        barrière *f* naturelle dans un
        aquifère
     d Grundwassersperre *f*;
        Untergrundsperre *f*

900 GROUNDWATER DISCHARGE
     f débit *m* en eau souterraine
     d Grundwasserspende *f*

901 GROUNDWATER DIVIDE
     in well hydraulics streamline with
     no flow, boundary of aquifer region
     contributing to well discharge
     f périmètre *m* d'appel
     d Grundwasserscheide *f*

902 GROUNDWATER DIVIDE
     dividing line between two ground
     water basins
     f ligne *f* de partage entre deux
        bassins hydrogéologiques
     d Grundwasserscheide *f*

     GROUNDWATER FLOW
     see groundwater runoff

903 GROUNDWATER INVENTORY
     complete quantitative accounting
     for all volumes of groundwater
     f bilan *m* des nappes souterraines
     d Grundwasserbestandsaufnahme *f*

904 GROUNDWATER LEVEL
     f niveau *m* de la nappe phréatique;
        niveau *m* piézométrique (d'une
        nappe libre)
     d Grundwasserspiegel *m*

905 GROUNDWATER MOUND
     f protubérance *f* de la nappe
     d Grundwassererhebung *f*

906 GROUNDWATER PROVINCE
     f province *f* des eaux souterraines
     d Grundwasserprovinz *f*

907 GROUNDWATER RECESSION
     f abaissement *m* de la nappe
        phréatique; décrue *f*
        souterraine
     d Grundwasserabsenkung *f*

908 GROUNDWATER RECESSION CURVE
     f courbe *f* d'abaissement;
        courbe *f* de tarissement
     d Grundwasserabsenkungskurve *f*

909 GROUNDWATER RESERVOIR
     reservoir in the void space beneath
     the water table
     f réservoir *m* en eaux souterraines
     d Grundwasserreservoir *n*;
        Grundwasserspeicher *m*

910 GROUNDWATER RUNOFF;
     GROUNDWATER FLOW
     runoff due to deep percolation
     from groundwater body
     f écoulement *m* souterrain
     d Grundwasserabfluss *m*

911 GUARD ELECTRODE
     f électrode *f* écran
     d Schirmelektrode *f*

912 GUIDE SHOE
     f sabot *m* de guidage
     d Führungsschuh *m*

913 GULLY
     deep erosional channel
     f chenal *m*
     d Rinne *f*; Erosionsrinne *f*

914 GUN PERFORATOR
     f perforatuer *m* à balles
     d Kugelschussapparat *m*

915 GUY WIRE
     fixed wire for the stabilization of
     a drilling rig
     f câble *m* d'ancrage
     d Halteseil *n*

H

916 HALF-LIFE
f demi-vie *f*
d Halbwertszeit *f*

917 HALITE
rock salt
f sel gemme *m*
d Steinsalz *n*

918 HALOMORPHIC SOIL
saline and alkali soils
f sol *m* halomorphe
d salzhaltiger Boden *m*

HAMMER, air see 41
-, drop see 595
-, water see 2936

919 HARDENING
process of induration
f endurcissement *m*
d Verhärtung *f*

HARDNESS, permanent see 2202
-, temporary see 2756
-, total see 2807

920 HARDNESS OF WATER
sum of calcium and magnesium ions
expressed as equivalent amount of
calcium carbonate ($CaCO_2$); property
to form insoluable salts of fatty
acid (soap)
f dureté *f*
d Härte *f*; Wasserhärte *f*

921 HARDPAN;
MORTAR BED
secondary calcium carbonate
cementations in lower part of soil
profile
f horizon *m* durci
d Konkretionskruste *f*;
   Felspanzerbildung *f*

922 HEAD
f charge *f*
d Höhe *f*; Druckhöhe *f*

HEAD, elevation see 641
-, energy see 651
-, friction see 796
-, hydraulic see 955
-, injection see 1037
-, piezometric see 2230

-, pressure see 2293
-, suction see 2694
-, velocity see 2890

923 HEAD LOSS
f perte *f* de charge
d Druckverlust *m*

924 HEAD WATER
upper reach of stream
f cours *m* supérieur
d Oberlauf *m*; Quellgebiet *n*

925 HEAT EXCHANGE
f échange *m* de chaleur
d Wärmeaustausch *m*

926 HEAT OF CONDENSATION
heat released in transforming a
substance from its vapor to its
liquid state
f chaleur *f* de condensation
d Kondensationswärme *f*

927 HEAT OF VAPORIZATION
heat necessary to change water
from liquid to gaseous state
f chaleur *f* de vaporisation
d Verdampfungwärme *f*

HEAT OF VAPORIZATION, latent
see 1130

928 HEAT TRANSFER
f transfert *m* de chaleur
d Wärmeumsatz *m*

HEAT, sensible see 2511

929 HELE-SHAW APPARATUS
parallel plate model to simulate
two-dimensional potential flow
f appareil *m* de Hele-Shaw
d Hele-Shawmodell *n*

930 HETEROGENEOUS
unequal spatial distribution of
aquifer properties
f hétérogène
d heterogen; ungleichförmig

931 HIGH BANK
f rive *f* haute
d Steilufer *n*

932 HIGH FLOW
     f débit *m* de crue
     d Hochwasserabfluss *m*

933 HIGH-WATER
     f crue *f*; hautes-eaux *f pl*
     d Hochwasser *n*

934 HODOGRAPH PLANE
     velocity plane, used in solution of
     free surface flow problems
     f plan *m* d'hodographe
     d Isotachenebene *f*

935 HOIST
     f treuil *m* de levage
     d Hebewerk *n*; Hebewinde *f*

936 HOISTING CABLE
     f câble *m* de levage
     d Förderseil *n*

937 HOISTING CAP
     removable cap with a ring to permit
     hoisting of drill pipe
     f tête *f* de levage
     d Hebekappe *f*

938 HOISTING CRANE
     f grue *f* de levage
     d Hebekran *m*

939 HOLDING TANK
     f bac *m* intercepteur
     d Auffangbehälter *m*

940 HOLE
     f trou *m*; trou *m* de forage;
        sonde *f*
     d Loch *n*; Bohrung *f*; Sonde *f*

     HOLE, bottom see 192
     -, crooked see 413
     -, dry see 601
     -, sink see 2563
     -, test see 2763
     -, uncased see 2857

941 HOMOGENEOUS
     even spatial distribution of aquifer
     properties
     f homogène
     d homogen; gleichförmig

942 HOMOGENEOUS FLUID
     fluid occurring in single phase
     f fluide *m* homogène
     d homogene Flüssigkeit *f*

     HOOK, drilling see 578

943 HOOK GAGE
     gage for the precise position
     measurement of liquid levels
     f pointe *f* de mesure
     d Stechpegel *m*

944 HOPPER
     f trémie *f*
     d Aufgabebunker *m*

     HORIZON, A- see 37
     -, B- see 175
     -, C- see 293
     -, D- see 493

945 HORNBLENDE
     see amphibole
     f hornblende *m*
     d Hornblende *f*

946 HORST
     block having been uplifted along its
     boundary faults
     f bloc *m* surélevé
     d Horst *m*; Hochscholle *f*

947 HORTON NUMBER
     expresses relative intensity of
     erosion process in drainage basin
     f nombre *m* de Horton
     d Horton-Zahl *f*

948 HOUSING
     f carter *m*
     d Gehäuse *n*

949 HUMIDITY
     f humidité *f*
     d Feuchte *f*

     HUMIDITY, absolute see 5
     -, relative .... of atmosphere
     see 2383

950 HYDRATION
     penetration of water into the crystal
     structure of a compound
     f hydration *f*
     d Hydratation *f*

951 HYDRAULIC CONDUCTIVITY
     ease with which water is conducted
     through an aquifer
     f conductivité *f* hydraulique;
        coefficient *m* de Darcy
     d hydraulische Leitfähigkeit *f*

952 HYDRAULIC DISCHARGE
     discharge of ground water through
     springs or wells

f   débit *m* hydraulique
d   hydraulischer Ausfluss *m*

953   HYDRAULIC FRACTURING
formation of artificial fractures
in rock system around a well by
high pressure fluid injections
f   fracturation *f* hydraulique
d   hydraulische Rissbildung *f*

954   HYDRAULIC GRADIENT
f   gradient *m* hydraulique
d   hydraulischer Gradient *m*

955   HYDRAULIC HEAD
energy per unit weight of fluid
f   énergie *f* hydraulique;
    hauteur *f* hydraulique
d   Fliessdruck *m*

956   HYDRAULIC JUMP
standing surge of water passing
from below critical depth in open
channel flow; abrupt depth variation
in rapidly varying channel flow
f   ressaut *m* hydraulique
d   hydraulischer Sprung *m*

957   HYDRAULIC PROFILE
vertical section of the piezometric
surface
f   section *f* hydraulique; profil *m*
    de dépression
d   hydraulisches Profil *n*

958   HYDRAULIC RADIUS
ratio of filled cross sectional area
to wetted perimeter
f   rayon *m* hydraulique
d   hydraulischer Radius *m*

959   HYDRAULIC ROTARY
rotary drilling method with
hydraulic drive
f   rotary *m* à commande hydraulique
d   Rotarybohren *n* mit hydraulischem
    Antrieb

960   HYDRAULICS
f   hydraulique *f*
d   Hydraulik *f*

961   HYDROCHLORIC ACID
f   acide *m* hydrochlorique
d   Salzsäure *f*

962   HYDRODYNAMIC CONDUCTIBILITY
f   conductibilité *f* hydrodynamique;
    hydroconductibilité *f*
d   hydrodynamische Leitfähigkeit *f*

963   HYDRODYNAMIC DISPERSION
dynamic dispersion of fluid
particles in flow through a porous
medium due to velocity changes in the
pore channels
f   dispersion *f* hydrodynamique
d   hydrodynamische Dispersion *f*

964   HYDROGEN BONDING
f   liaison *f* hydrogène
d   Wasserstoffbrückenbindung *f*

965   HYDROGEN-ION CONCENTRATION
pH
f   concentration *f* en ions d'hydrogèr
d   Wasserstoffionenkonzentration *f*

966   HYDROGEN SULFIDE
H_2S
f   hydrogène *m* sulfuré
d   Schwefelwasserstoff *m*

967   HYDROGEOCHEMISTRY
geochemistry as related to the
occurrence of water
f   hydrogéochimie *f*
d   Hydrogeochemie *f*

968   HYDROGEOLOGY
study of subsurface waters in their
geological context
f   hydrogéologie *f*
d   Hydrogeologie *f*

969   HYDROGRAPH
time record of stream discharge
at a given cross section of stream
or of stream surface elevation at
a given point
f   hydrogramme *m*
d   Ganglinie *f* des Wasserstandes;
    Abflussganglinie *f*; Hydrograph *

HYDROGRAPH, characteristic
see 282
-, discharge see 517
-, simple see 2559
-, stage see 2633
-, synthetic unit see 2742
-, well see 2992

970   HYDROGRAPH SEPARATION
separation of hydrograph into its
different components to analyze
flow contributions
f   décomposition *f* de l'hydro-
    gramme; analyse *f* de
    l'hydrogramme
d   Aufspaltung *f* der Abflussgang-
    linie

971　HYDROGRAPHY
geographical description of water
bodies on earth's surface
f　hydrographie *f*
d　beschreibende Gewässerkunde *f*;
　　Hydrographie *f*

972　HYDROLACCOLITH
mounds raised by formation of
ice lenses in permafrost soil
f　laccolith *m* de glace
.d　Eislakkolith *m*

973　HYDROLOGIC BARRIER
lithologic formation preventing
horizontal movement of ground
water
f　barrière *f* hydrologique
d　Grundwasserbarriere *f*

974　HYDROLOGIC BUDGET
quantitative accounting of all
water volumes and their change
with time for a given basin or
province
f　bilan *m* hydrologique
d　Wasserhaushalt *m*

975　HYDROLOGIC CYCLE
f　cycle *m* hydrologique
d　hydrologischer Kreislauf *m*

976　HYDROLOGIC EQUATION
f　équation *m* hydrologique
d　hydrologische Grundgleichung *f*

977　HYDROLOGY
study of atmospheric, surface,
and subsurface waters and their
connection with the water cycle
f　hydrologie *f*
d　Gewässerkunde *f*;
　　Hydrologie *f*

978　HYDROLYSIS
f　hydrolyse *f*
d　Hydrolyse *f*

979　HYDROMETEOROLOGY
meteorology dealing with water in
the atmosphere
f　hydrométéorologie *f*
d　Hydrometeorologie *f*

980　HYDROMETRIC STATION
station at which usually a number
of hydrometric measurements
are performed
f　station *f* hydrométrique
d　hydrometrische Messtelle *f*

981　HYDROMETRY
science of water measurements
f　hydrométrie *f*
d　Hydrometrie *f*

982　HYDROPHILIC
having great affinity for water
f　hydrophile
d　wasseranziehend

983　HYDROPHOBIC
repelling water
f　hydrophobe
d　wasserabstossend

984　HYDROPHYTE
plant requiring large amount of
moisture for growth
f　hydrophyte *f*
d　Wasserpflanze *f*; Hydrophyte *f*

985　HYDROSPHERE
part of earth containing liquid or
solid water
f　hydrosphère *f*
d　Hydrosphäre *f*

986　HYDROSTATIC PRESSURE
f　pression *f* hydrostatique
d　hydrostatischer Druck *m*

987　HYETOGRAPH
graph of rainfall intensity against
time
f　hyétogramme *m*
d　Ganglinie *f* der Niederschlags-
　　intensität

988　HYGROMETER
apparatus for the direct measurement
of the relative humidity in the
atmosphere
f　hygromètre *m*
d　Hygrometer *n*

989　HYGROSCOPIC COEFFICIENT
amount of absorbed water on
surface of soil particles in an
atmosphere of 50% relative
humidity at 25°C
f　coefficient *m* hygroscopique
d　Hygroskopizität *f*

990　HYGROSCOPICITY
f　pouvoir *m* hygroscopique
d　Hygroskopizität *f*;
　　Wasseranziehungskraft *f*

991　HYGROSCOPIC NUCLEUS
small solid particle around which

water condensates (cloud
formation)
f noyeau *m* hygroscopique
d hygroskopischer Kern *m*

992 HYGROSCOPIC WATER
condensed water at solid surface
f eau *f* hygroscopique
d hygroskopisches Wasser *n*

993 HYPOLIMNION
deep layer in stratified water
f hypolimnion *m*
d Hypolimnion *n*

994 HYSTERESIS
f hystérésis *f*
d Hysteresis *f*; Remanenzerschei-
nung *f*

HYSTERESIS, capillary see 240

I

995 ICE
     crystallized water, below freezing
     point
     f glace *f*
     d Eis *n*

     ICE, anchor see 72
     -, dry see 602
     -, ground see 72
     -, interstitial see 1068

996 ICE CAP
     f calotte *f* glaciaire
     d Eiskappe *f*

997 IGNEOUS ACTIVITY
     all processes connected with the
     intrusion and formation of igneous
     rocks
     f activité *f* magmatique;
        volcanisme *m*
     d Vulkanismus *m* (im weiteren
        Sinne)

998 IGNEOUS ROCK
     rocks formed by solidification of
     intrusive or extrusive molten
     magma
     f roche *f* ignée
     d Magmagestein *n*

999 ILLITE
     a clay mineral
     f illite *m*
     d Illit *m*

1000 IMAGE WELL
     imaginary well in the complex plane
     f puits *m* fictif
     d imaginärer Brunnen *m*

1001 IMBIBITION
     fluid displacement in porous media
     due to capillary forces alone
     f imbibition *f*
     d kapillarer Verdrängungsvorgang *m*;
        Imbibition *f*

1002 IMMISCIBLE
     quality of liquids showing clear
     interface at contact with each other;
     not miscible
     f immiscible
     d nicht mischbar

1003 IMPEDANCE
     apparent resistance of a conductive
     system when alternating current is
     applied
     f impédance *f*
     d induktiver Widerstand *m*;
        Impedanz *f*

1004 IMPELLER
     f roue *f* à aubes
     d Schaufelrad *n*; Laufrad *n*

1005 IMPERMEABLE
     impervious to flow of fluids such
     as an aquiclude
     f imperméable
     d undurchlässig

1006 IMPERVIOUS
     not permitting passage of water
     f non perméable
     d undurchlässig

1007 IMPERVIOUS LENS
     impermeable, lens-shaped body of
     sediment in an otherwise permeable
     aquifer
     f lentille *f* imperméable
     d undurchlässige Linse *f*

1008 IMPORTED WATER
     water coming from outside of a
     groundwater basin under consideration
     f eaux *f pl* d'importation
     d eingeführtes Wasser *n*;
        Fremdwasser *n*

1009 IMPOUND
     collect water by damming
     f refouler; emmagasiner
     d stauen; eindämmen

1010 INCLINOMETER
     instrument to measure the inclination
     of a surface
     f inclinomètre *m*
     d Neigungsmesser *m*

1011 INCOHERENT MATERIAL
     unconsolidated material
     f matériel *m* non-consolidé
     d loses Material *n*; nicht
        zusammenhängendes Material *n*

1012 INCOMPRESSIBLE
    f incompressible
    d inkompressibel

1013 INCRUSTATION
deposition of mineral matter by
water
    f incrustation *f*
    d Krustenbildung *f*

1014 INDUCED ACTIVITY
activity or response of a system
that has been subject to an artifical
excitation
    f activité *f* induite
    d induzierte Aktivität *f*

1015 INDUCED INFILTRATION
increased infiltration from a
surface water body due to planned
lowering of the original water table
    f infiltration *f* provoquée
    d künstliche Einsickerung *f*

1016 INDUCED RECHARGE
method of withdrawing ground water
in strategic points to induce natural
recharge
    f alimentation *f* initiée
    d induzierte Grundwasseranrei-
       cherung *f*

1017 INDUCTION
    f induction *f*
    d Induktion *f*

1018 INDUCTION LOG
resistivity log using induced
currents
    f diagraphie *f* par induction
    d Induktionslog *n*

1019 INDURATED ROCK
rock hardened and solidified by a
diagenetic process
    f roche *f* endurcie
    d verfestigtes Gestein *n*

1020 INDUSTRIAL DIAMOND
    f diamant *m* industriel
    d Industriediamant *m*

1021 INDUSTRIAL WATER
    f eaux *fpl* d'usage
    d Brauchwasser *n*; Nutzwasser *n*

1022 INFILTRABILITY
ease of infiltration
    f capacité *f* d'infiltration
    d Eindringkapazität *f*

1023 INFILTRATION
flow of water through soil surface
into underground
    f infiltration *f*
    d Einsickerung *f*

INFILTRATION, induced see 1015

1024 INFILTRATION BASIN
basin in which water is spread for
recharge
    f bassin *m* d'épandage
    d Versickerungsbecken *n*

1025 INFILTRATION CAPACITY
maximum rate at which soil can
absorb precipitation for given
conditions
    f capacité *f* d'absorption
    d Einsickerfähigkeit *f*

1026 INFILTRATION GALLERY
horizontal conduit to intercept
groundwater
    f galerie *f* d'infiltration
    d Infiltrationsstrecke *f*

1027 INFILTRATION INDEX
average rate of infiltration throughout a given rain storm
    f indice *m* infiltration
    d Infiltrationsindex *m*

1028 INFILTRATION WATER
water above watertable with
predominantly vertical downward
component of motion
    f eaux *fpl* d'infiltration
    d Sickerwasser *n*

1029 INFILTROMETER
apparatus measuring the amount of
infiltration
    f infiltromètre *m*
    d Infiltrometer *n*

1030 INFILTROMETER TEST
    f essai *m* d'infiltromètre
    d Infiltrometeruntersuchung *f*

1031 INFLOW
    f afflux *m*; affluence *f*
    d Zufluss *m*

INFLOW, lateral see 1134

1032 INFLUENT STREAM,
LOSING STREAM
stream recharging groundwater
reservoir

f   rivière *f* alimentant la
    nappe
d   wasserabgebender Fluss *m*

1033 INITIAL ABSTRACTION
      maxiumum amount of rainfall
      absorbed without producing runoff;
      initial losses
      f   pertes *f pl* initiales
      d   Anfangsverluste *f pl*

1034 INITIAL CONDITIONS
      f   conditions *f pl* initiales
      d   Anfangsbedingungen *f pl*

1035 INITIAL PRESSURE
      f   pression *f* initiale
      d   Anfangsdruck *m*

1036 INJECT, TO
      introduction of pressurized fluids
      into a porous subsurface formation
      f   injecter
      d   einpressen

1037 INJECTION HEAD
      swivel head connector through
      which drilling fluid is injected into
      the drill pipe
      f   tête *f* d'injection
      d   Spülkopf *m*

      INJECTION METHOD, mercury
      see 2028

1038 INJECTIVITY
      capacity of a well or formation to
      accomodate pumped in liquid
      f   injectivité *f*
      d   Schluckfähigkeit *f*; Aufnahme-
          fähigkeit *f*

1039 INLAND LAKE
      f   lac *m* intérieur
      d   Binnensee *m*

1040 INLET CHAMBER
      f   chambre *f* d'aspiration
      d   Saugraum *m*

1041 INLET OPENING
      f   orifice *m* d'adduction
      d   Einflussöffnung *f*

1042 INSIDE DIAMETER
      f   diamètre *m* intérieur
      d   Innendruchmesser *m*;
          lichte Weite *f*

1043 INSOLATION
      irradiation by the sun

f   insolation *f*
d   Insolation *f*; Sonnenbestrahlung *f*

1044 INSTABILITY PHENOMENON
      f   phénomène *m* d'instabilité
      d   Instabilitätserscheinung *f*

1045 INSULATED STREAM
      stream neither receiving nor
      abstracting water from ground water
      body because of an impermeable bed
      f   rivière *f* isolée
      d   isolierter Fluss *m*

1046 INSULATING SLEEVE
      f   gaine *f* isolante
      d   Schutzhülle *f*; Isolierhülle *f*

1047 INSULATION JOINT
      f   joint *m* isolant
      d   Isolierverbindung *f*

1048 INTAKE AREA
      area where inflow to aquifer takes
      place
      f   surface *f* d'alimentation
      d   Einzugsgebiet *n*

1049 INTEGRATING CIRCUIT
      circuit averaging scintillometer
      pulses over known time interval
      f   circuit *m* intégrant
      d   Integratorschaltung *f*

      INTENSITY, rain see 2333
      -, rainfall see 2329
      -, relief see 2386
      -, shear see 2528

1050 INTERAQUIFER FLOW
      flow between aquifers through
      fracture openings or through
      wellbore
      f   exutoire *m* souterrain
      d   Zwischenfluss *m*

1051 INTERBEDDED
      pertaining to beds or sedimentary
      material intercalated in a parallel
      fashion into a main stratum
      f   intercalé
      d   mit Schichteinschaltungen *f pl*
          versehen; mit Zwischenmitteln
          n pl versehen

1052 INTERBEDDING
      bed between layers of different
      material
      f   couche *f* intercalée
      d   Zwischenmittel *n*

1053 INTERCALATED BED
f couche *f* intercalaire
d Zwischenmittel *n*

1054 INTERCEPT
f intercepte *m*; point *m* d'interception
d Schnittpunkt *m*

1055 INTERCEPTION
abstraction of direct rainfall on
vegetation cover
f interception *f*
d Interzeption *f*; Abfangen *n*;
Tropfenabfang *m*

1056 INTERCEPTION LOSS
part of rainfall retained by aerial
portion of vegetative cover
f perte *f* d'interception
d Interzeptionsverlust *m*;
Tropfenabfang *m*

1057 INTERDIGITATION
lateral interlocking of sedimentary
series
f interdigitation *f*
d Verzahnung *f*; fingerförmiges
Eingreifen *n*

1058 INTERFACE
contact plane of two immiscible
liquids
f interface *m*
d Grenzfläche *f*

1059 INTERFACIAL TENSION
f tension *f* interfaciale
d Grenzflächenspannung *f*

1060 INTERFLOW
subsurface runoff
f écoulement *m* hypodermique
d unechter Grundwasserabfluss *m*

1061 INTERGRANULAR STRESS
stress between grains in solid
matrix
f tension *f* intergranulaire
d Zwischenkornspannung *f*

1062 INTERMITTENT SPRING
spring flowing at intervals
f source *f* intermittente
d intermittierende Quelle *f*

1063 INTERMITTENT STREAM
stream flowing intermittently
f fleuve *m* intermittent
d intermittierender Fluss *m*;
periodisch fliessender Strom *m*

1064 INTERMONTANE BASIN
basin lying between two mountain
ranges
f bassin *m* d'entremont
d Zwischengebirgszone *f*

1065 INTERNAL DRAINAGE
drainage in a closed basin not
reaching the sea
f drainage *m* endoréique
d Abflusslosigkeit *f*

1066 INTERRUPTED STREAM
stream interrupted over space;
discontinous stream
f rivière *f* interrompue
d versinkender Fluss *m*

1067 INTERSTICE
small interstitial space between
solid rock matrix particles
f espace *m* interstitiel
d Zwischenraum *m*; Porenraum *m*

INTERSTICE, original see 2141
-, secondary see 2492

1068 INTERSTITIAL ICE
ice occurring below the surface in
the pores of the soil
f glace *f* interstitielle
d Poreneis *n*

1069 INTERSTITIAL WATER
water held in small wedge like
interstices at grain contact
f eau *f* angulaire; eau *f* cunéiforn
d Porenwinkelwasser *n*;
Zwickelwasser *n*

1070 INTRAPERMAFROST WATER
ground water within the permafrost
horizon
f eau *f* dans la zone du pergelisol
d Grundwasser *n* im Permafrostbe

1071 INTRINSIC PERMEABILITY
characteristic resistance to flow
of porous medium alone, independe
of fluid properties
f perméabilité *f* intrinsèque
d absolute Permeabilität *f*

1072 INTRUSION
body of ingenous rock cutting throu
or replacing older rock
f intrusion *f*
d Intrusion *f*; Eindringung *f*

INTRUSION, sea water see 2491

1073 INTRUSIVE ROCK
igneous rock remaining below the
earth's surface
f roche *f* intrusive
d Intrusivgestein *n*

1074 INUNDATION
covering of an area by flood waters
f inondation *f*
d Überschwemmung *f*

1075 INVADED ZONE
in electric logging zone into which
an appreciable amount of mud
filtrate has penetrated
f zone *f* envahie
d geflutete Zone *f*

1076 INVASION
in logging penetration of a fluid
into the porous medium
f invasion *f*
d Eindringen *n*

INVASION, water see 2937

1077 INVASION DEPTH
depth to which drilling mud
filtrate penetrates into formation
f profondeur *f* envahie
d Eindringungstiefe *f*

1078 INVERSION
negative lapse rate (increase in
temperature with altitude)
f inversion *f*
d Inversion *f*; Temperatur-
umkehr *f*

INVERTED WELL
see recharge well

1079 ION MOBILITY
ease with which ions move in an
electrolytical solution
f mobilité *f* des ions
d Mobilität *f* der Ionen

1080 IRREDUCIBLE SATURATION
lowest water saturation obtainable
by mechanical reduction methods
f saturation *f* irréductible
d irreduzierbare Sättigung *f*

1081 IRRIGATION
artificial watering of fields for
crop production
f irrigation *f*
d Bewässerung *f*

1082 IRRIGATION REQUIREMENT
water needed for crop production
exclusive of precipitation
f demande *f* en eau d'irrigation
d Bewässerungsbedarf *m*

1083 IRROTATIONAL FLOW
potential flow, flow with no
rotational component
f écoulement *m* irrotationnel
d wirbelfreier Fluss *m*

1084 ISOBATH
line of equal depth
f isobathe *f*
d Isobathe *f*; Tiefenlinie *f*

1085 ISOCHRONE
line connecting waterlevel in
observation wells for one given
instant
f isochrone *f*
d Isochrone *f*; Zeitgleiche *f*

1086 ISOHYET
line of equal rainfall
f ligne *f* isohyète; courbe *f* isohyète
d Regengleiche *f*; Isohyete *f*

1087 ISOPIESTIC LINE
contour on piezometric surface
connecting points of equal static
level
f isopièze *f*; hydroisohypse *f*
d Grundwassergleiche *f*

1088 ISOPLETH
line of equal distance from point
of outflow of a basin
f ligne *f* isoplèthe
d Abstandsgleiche *f*

1089 ISOPOTAL LINE
line of equal infiltration capacity
f ligne *f* isopotale
d Linie *f* gleicher Eindringkapazität

1090 ISOTHERM
line of equal temperatures
f isotherme *f*
d Isotherme *f*

1091 ISOTOPE
f isotope *m*
d Isotop *n*

1092 ISOTROPIC
quality of aquifer where properties
remain the same in all directions
f isotropique
d isotropisch

J

1093 JACK
f cric *m*
d Hebevorrichtung *f*; Winde *f*

1094 JARS
in cable drilling: interlocked
gliding links above drill collar
permitting stuck bit to be jerked
free
f coulisse *f* de forage
d Rutschschere *f*

1095 JET
f jet *m*
d Strahl *m*; Düse *f*

1096 JET BIT
drilling tool where some of the
abrasive effect is due to jets
f outil à jet *m*
d Düsenmeissel *m*

1097 JET PUMP
f pompe *f* à jet
d Düsenstrahlpumpe *f*

1098 JETTED WELL
well formed by cutting action of a
water stream or jet
f puits *m* creusé par jets d'eau
d Spülbohrung *f*

1099 JOINT
junction or connection of mechanical
elements (as drill pipe and tubing)
f joint *m*
d Verbindung *f*

1100 JOINT
fracture in rock along the plane
of which no movement or dislocation
has taken place
f joint *m*; diaclase *f*
d Kluft *f*; Diaklase *f*

JOINT, bedding see 166
-, casing see 254
-, cooling see 383
-, expansion see 690
-, insulation see 1047
-, reducing see 2373
-, threaded see 2778
-, tool see 2799
-, welded see 2981

1101 JOINT PLANE
f plan *m* de diaclase
d Kluftfläche *f*

1102 JUNCTION POTENTIAL
electrochemical potential
developed at the junction of two
solutions of different concentration
f potentiel *m* de jonction
d Berührungspotential *n*

1103 JURASSIC
geologic period of the Mesozoic era
f Jurassique *m*
d Jura *n*

1104 JUVENILE WATER
water that has not been part of
hydrosphere before, derived from
interior of earth
f eaux *fpl* juvéniles
d juveniles Wasser *n*

K

1105 **KAME**
stratified glacial sand and gravel
deposit forming small hill
f   kame *m*
d   Kame *f*

1106 **KAOLIN**
common clay mineral
f   kaolin *m*
d   Kaolin *n*

1107 **KARST**
limestone terrane marked by very
large solution openings
f   karst *m*
d   Karst *m*

1108 **KARST REGION**
f   région *f* karstique
d   Karstgebiet *n*

1109 **KELLEY**
square section of drill pipe
transmitting rotary movement from
rotary table to the drill stem
f   tige *f* carrée
d   Mitnehmerstange *f*

1110 **KICK**
short deflection of a pointer or trace
f   top *m*
d   Ausschlag *m*

1111 **KINEMATIC SIMILARITY**
f   similitude *f* cinématique
d   kinematische Ähnlichkeit *f*

1112 **KLINKENBERG EFFECT**
slip of gas molecules at pore wall
giving apparently higher permeability
than obtained by liquid measurements
f   effet *m* Klinkenberg
d   Klinkenbergeffekt *m*

L

1113 LABORATORY COEFFICIENT
OF PERMEABILITY;
STANDARD COEFFICIENT OF
PERMEABILITY
defined for controlled temperature
conditions (60°F) gpd per f² under
unit gradient (see Meinzer unit)
f coefficient *m* de perméabilité du
laboratoire
d Labor - Durchlässigkeitsbeiwert *m*

1114 LABORATORY DATA
f données *fpl* de laboratoire;
données *fpl* expérimentales
d Versuchswerte *mpl*;
Laboratoriumsdaten *fpl*

1115 LACCOLITH
dome shaped intrusive rock body
f laccolith *m*
d Lakkolith *m*

1116 LACUSTRINE
pertaining to lakes
f lacustre
d lakustre

1117 LACUSTRINE FORMATION
sedimentary formation in a lake
f formation *f* lacustre
d lakustre Bildung *f*; lakustre
Formation *f*

1118 LAGOON
body of relatively shallow water
near sea shore, with or without
direct connection to the sea
f lagune *f*
d Lagune *f*; Haff *n*

1119 LAG TIME
time lapse between the onset of
a given event and the produced
results; in drilling: time for
cuttings to be carried out from the
bottom hole to the surface
f retard *m*; temps *m* de réponse
d Verzögerung *f*

1120 LAKE
body of fresh inland water
f lac *m*
d See *m*; Binnensee *m*

LAKE, crater see 399
-, inland see 1039
-, reservoir see 2392
-, salt see 2457
-, volcanic see 2904

1121 LAMINAR FLOW
f écoulement *m* laminaire
d laminare Strömung *f*;
Schichtströmung *f*

1122 LAMINATION
layering or very thin bedding of
sedimentary rocks
f lamination *f*
d Schichtung *f*; Lamination *f*

1123 LAND-FORM
topographic feature of the earth's
surface
f forme *f* morphologique
d Landform *f*

1124 LAND PAN
evaporation pan to measure
evaporation from a land surface;
pan mounted on land surface
f bac *m* d'évaporation au dessus
du terrain
d Landverdunstungskessel *m*

1125 LANDSLIDE
sliding down of earth and rock on
a slope
f glissement *m* de terrain
d Landrutsch *m*; Hangrutsch *m*

1126 LAND SUBSIDENCE
subsidence of surface (due to
pumping of underlying aquifer or
other mining activities)
f affaissement *m* de la surface;
subsidence *f* de la surface
d Oberflächenabsenkung *f*

1127 LAND SURFACE
part of lithosphere usually not
covered by water
f surface *f* terrestre
d Landoberfläche *f*

1128 LAND-USE
particular utilization of a surface
especially with respect to its
influence on the hydrologic cycle

f   utilisation *f* des terres
d   Landverwendung *f*; Landnutzung *f*

1129   LAPSE RATE
vertical temperature gradient in
the atmosphere
f   gradient *m* vertical de la
température
d   vertikaler Temperaturgradient *m*

1130   LATENT HEAT OF VAPORIZATION
f   chaleur *f* de vaporisation latente
d   latente Verdampfungswärme *f*

1131   LATERAL CORING
method of taking samples from the
sidewall of the well
f   prélèvement *m* latéral
d   Probenahme *f* aus der Bohrlochswand

1132   LATERAL CURVE
resistivity log taken with long
effective spacing of electrodes
f   diagramme *m* latéral
d   Laterologaufnahme *f*

1133   LATERAL GRADATION
f   nivellement *m* latéral
d   seitliche Einebnung *f*

1134   LATERAL INFLOW
f   afflux *m* latéral
d   seitlicher Zufluss *m*

1135   LATERAL MORAINE
galcial deposit at flank of a glacier,
often constituted by debris from
valley walls
f   moraine *f* latérale
d   Seitenmoräne *f*

1136   LATERITE
tropical ferruginous clay soil
f   latérite *f*
d   Laterit *m*

1137   LATERITIC SOIL
red colored soil with high iron
oxide content
f   sol *m* latéritique
d   Lateriterde *f*

LAVA, block see 188
-, pillow see 2233

1138   LAVA BED
lava flow of considerable areal
extend and relatively small
thickness

f   couche *f* de lave
d   Lavaschicht *f*

LAVA CRUST, congealed see 353

1139   LAVA FLOW PLATEAU
f   plate-forme *f* d'effusion
d   Ergusstafel *f*

1140   LAVA TUBE
empty tubular supply channel from
which liquid lava has drained
f   tunnel *m* de lave
d   Lavatube *f*; Lavaröhre *f*

1141   LAYER
sheetlike deposit of sediment;
bed or stratum of rock
f   couche *f*
d   Schicht *f*; Lage *f*

LAYER, boundary see 196

1142   LEACHING
washing out by dissolution
f   lessivage *m*
d   Auslaugung *f*; Laugung *f*

1143   LEAK
opening in an aquiclude that
permits penetration of water from
other formations into main aquifer
f   fuite *f*
d   Leck *n*; Undichtigkeit *f*

1144   LEAK DETECTOR
f   détecteur *m* de fuites
d   Suchgerät *n*

1145   LEAKAGE FACTOR
factor describing leakage flow into
or out of leaky aquifer
f   facteur *m* de fuite
d   Undichtigkeitsfaktor *m*

1146   LEAKANCE
leakage coefficient, ratio of
hydraulic conductivity of semiconfining
stratum to its thickness
f   coefficient *m* de fuite
d   Undichtigkeitszahl *f*

1147   LEAKY AQUIFER
aquifer overlain or underlain by
semipermeable strata from or into
which water will flow
f   couche *f* aquifère à fuites
d   leckender Grundwasserleiter *m*

1148   LEVEE
artificial bank to prevent overbank

flow of a river
f   levée *f*; digue *f*
d   Damm *m*; Deich *m*

LEVEE, natural see 2100

1149   LEVEL
surface of water in a well or standing
reservoir
f   niveau *m*
d   Höhe *f*; Spiegel *m*

LEVEL, base see 150
-, ground see 889
-, groundwater see 904
-, mean sea see 2004
-, salinity see 2453
-, sea see 2487
-, water see 2939

1150   LIFT
vertical pumping distance between
water level in the well to surface
f   hauteur *f* d'aspiration
d   Saughöhe *f*

LIFT, air see 42
-, suction see 2695

1151   LIGHT SPOT
reflected light spot from a galvanometer mirror
f   spot *m* lumineux
d   Lichtpunkt *m*

1152   LIMESTONE
sedimentary deposit of carbonate
rock
f   calcaire *m*
d   Kalkstein *m*

LIMESTONE, algal see 50
-, argillaceous see 109

1153   LIMITING VALUE
f   valeur *f* limite
d   Grenzwert *m*

1154   LIMNOLOGY
study of lakes
f   limnologie *f*
d   Limnologie *f*

LINE, air see 43
-, bailing see 2462
-, base see 152
-, casing see 255
-, contour see 374
-, crest see 404
-, drilling see 579

-, energy see 652
-, energy grade see 650
-, equipotential see 664
-, fault see 707
-, isopiestic see 1087
-, isopotal see 1089
-, recharge see 2358
-, regression see 2380
-, sand see 2462
-, shale see 2523
-, snow see 2583
-, suction see 2697
-, wet see 3007
-, wire see 3020

1155   LIQUID
incompressible or very little
compressible fluid
f   liquide *m*
d   Flüssigkeit *f*

LIQUID, mother see 2079

1156   LITHOLOGIC FACTOR
factor influencing composition,
texture, and sequence of rock types
f   facteur *m* lithologique
d   lithologischer Faktor *m*

1157   LITHOLOGY
physical properties and aspect of a
rock
f   lithologie *f*
d   Lithologie *f*

1158   LITHOSOL
rocky soil
f   sol *m* rocheux
d   Steinboden *m*; Felsboden *m*

1159   LITHOSPHERE
part of earth's crust containing
solid rocks
f   lithosphère *f*
d   Lithosphäre *f*

1160   LITTORAL ZONE
coastal strip
f   littoral *m*
d   Litoral *n*; Küstenbereich *m*

LOAD, base see 153
-, basin see 168
-, contact see 364
-, natural see 2101
-, permanent see 2203
-, permissible see 2210
-, saltation see 2455
-, suspended see 2730
-, traction see 168

-, wash see 2917
-, waste see 2920

LOADS, external see 697

1161 LOAM
calcareous clay
f limon *m*
d Lehm *m*

1162 LODGEMENT TILL
till deposited from slowly melting
ice at base of glaciers
f argile *m* à blocaux; éboulis *m*
glaciaire
d Grundmoränengeschiebe *n*

1163 LOESS
eolian deposit of very fine sand
f loess *m*
d Löss *m*

1164 LOG
record of drilling operations and
formations drilled
f log *n*; diagraphie *f*
d Bohrprotokoll *n*; Log *n*

LOG, acoustic see 18
-, caliper see 231
-, contact see 365
-, driller's see 570
-, drilling-time see 583
-, electric see 633
-, fluid-velocity see 767
-, gamma see 810
-, geologic see 833
-, induction see 1018
-, neutron see 2108
-, radioactivity see 2324
-, restitivity see 2399
-, temperature see 2754

1165 LOGGING CABLE
f câble *m* de diagraphie
d Messkabel *n*

1166 LOGGING TRUCK
truck in which all logging, recording,
and control instruments are housed
f camion *m* d'enregistrement;
camion *m* de diagraphie
d Messwagen *m*

1167 LOG INTERPRETATION
f interprétation *f* des diagraphies
d Logauswertung *f*

1168 LONGITUDINAL FAULT
fault having the same direction of
strike as surrounding strata

f faille *f* longitudinale
d Längsverwerfung *f*

1169 LONGITUDINAL WAVE
f onde *f* longitudinale
d Longitudinalwelle *f*

1170 LOOSEST PACKING
three dimensional arrangement of
particles with highest possible void
volume per unit cell
f arrangement *m* le plus lâche;
empilement *m* le plus lâche
d poröseste Packung *f*

LOSING STREAM, see influent stream

LOSS, canal see 233
-, dielectric see 500
-, evaporation see 679
-, head see 923
-, interception see 1056
-, mud see 2090
-, well see 2995

1171 LOWER CONFINING BED
impermeable bed underlying an
aquifer
f mur *m* imperméable (d'un aquifer);
imperméable *m*; substratum *m*
imperméable
d Grundwassersohle *f*; Sohlschicht *f*

1172 LOWER COURSE
part of water course near discharge
point
f cours *m* inférieur
d Unterlauf *m*

1173 LOW FLOW
lowest sustained flow during base
runoff conditions of a river
f débit *m* d'étiage
d Niedrigwasserabfluss *m*

1174 LOW WATER
f basses-eaux *f pl*
d Niedrigwasser *n*

1175 LYSIMETER
experimental installation to evaluate
infiltration and evapotranspiration
under field or natural conditions
f lysimètre *m*
d Lysimeter *n*

M

1176 MACROPORE
pore with dimensions such that
capillary forces become less
important during flow
f   macropore *m*
d   Grosspore *f*; Makropore *f*

1177 MAGMA
molten rock substance formed within
the earth from which igneous rocks
originate
f   magma *m*
d   Magma *n*

1178 MAGMATIC WATER
water in or derived from magma
f   eaux *f pl* magmatiques
d   magmatisches Wasser *n*;
endogenes Wasser *n*

1179 MAGNETIC SURVEY
geophysical method of mapping
magnetic fields
f   étude *f* magnétique
d   Magnetometerkartierung *f*

1180 MAGNETIC SUSCEPTIBILITY
f   susceptibilité *f* magnétique
d   magnetische Suszeptibilität *f*

1181 MAGNETITE
accessory mineral of igneous rocks,
iron ore
f   magnétite *m*
d   Magnetit *m*

MAIN, collecting see 324

1182 MAIN CHANNEL FLOW
f   écoulement *m* du cours principal
d   Wasserführung *f* im Haupt-
flusslauf

1183 MAIN GATE
f   vanne *f* maîtresse
d   Hauptschieber *m*

1184 MANOMETER
pressure measuring device,
pressure gauge
f   manomètre *m*
d   Manometer *n*

1185 MAP
f   carte *f*
d   Karte *f*

MAPPING, conformal see 352
-, surface see 2718

1186 MARBLE
dense metamorphic calc-silicate or
magnesia rock
f   marbre *m*
d   Marmor *m*

1187 MARINE WATER
ocean water having invaded coastal
aquifers; sea water
f   eau *f* de mer
d   Meerwasser *n*

MARK, bench see 172
-, rippel see 2412

1188 MARKER BED
bed with characteristic features that
can be followed over large areas
for identification purposes
f   couche *f* caractéristique
d   Leithorizont *m*

1189 MARL
calcarous clay
f   marle *f*
d   Mergel *m*

1190 MASS CONSERVATION
f   conservation *f* massique
d   Massenerhaltung *f*

1191 MASS CURVE
graph of cumulative values of a
hydrological quantity against time
f   courbe *f* de masse; courbe *f* des
valeurs cumulées
d   Summenkurve *f*; Mengenlinie *f*;
Summenganglinie *f*

1192 MASS DENSITY
mass per unit volume of a substance
f   densité *f* massique
d   Dichte *f*

1193 MASS FLOWMETER
measuring device for mass flow
rates
f   débimètre *m* massique
d   Massenflussmessgerät *n*

1194 MASSIVE STRUCTURE
homogeneous structure without any
oriented features

f   structure *f* massive
d   massige Textur *f*

1195   MASS TRANSFER
f   transfert *m* massique
d   Stoffübertragung *f*

1196   MAST
f   mât *m* de forage
d   Mast *m*; Bohrmast *m*

1197   MATCH POINT
common point in Theis' superposition method
f   point *m* arbitraire
d   Bezugspunkt *m*

1198   MAXIMUM BASIN RELIEF
elevation difference between basin
mouth and highest point within
basin perimeter
f   relief *m* maximum
d   grösster Reliefunterschied *m*

1199   MAXIMUM DISCHARGE
maximum dischàrge of a river
during a flood
f   débit *m* de pointe
d   Spitzenabfluss *m*

2000   MAXIMUM EVENT
f   événement *m* maximum
d   Maximalereignis *n*

MEAN, annual see 85
-, arithmetic see 111
-, geometric see 834

2001   MEANDER
looplike bend in river due to lateral
erosion activities
f   méandre *m*
d   Mäander *m*

2002   MEANDER BELT
zone within which meandering of
stream occurs
f   zone *f* des méandres
d   Mäandergürtel *m*

2003   MEAN DEVIATION
linear mean of absolute deviations
f   écart *m* moyen
d   lineare Streuung *f*

2004   MEAN SEA LEVEL
f   niveau *m* moyen des mers
d   mittlere Meereshöhe *f*

2005   MEAN VALUE
statistical average, measure of

central tendency
f   valeur *f* moyenne
d   Mittelwert *m*

2006   MEASURE
f   mesure *f*
d   Messung *f*

MEASUREMENT, wading see 2911

2007   MEASURING CIRCUIT
f   circuit *m* de mesure
d   Messkreis *m*

2008   MEASURING COIL
f   bobine *f* de mesure
d   Messpule *f*

2009   MEASURING DUCT
f   canal *m* de jaugeage
d   Messgerinne *n*

2010   MEASURING FLUME
artificial channel used for discharge
measurements
f   jaugeur *m*
d   Messrinne *f*

2011   MEASURING REEL
f   treuil *m* de jaugeage
d   Messwinde *f*

2012   MEASURING STICK
f   échelle *f*
d   Pegel *m*; Messlatte *f*

2013   MEASURING TUBE
f   tube *m* à mesure; éprouvette *f*
d   Messzylinder *m*

2014   MEASURING WEIR
device to measure flow rates
indirectly through the weir head
f   déversoir *m* à mesure
d   Messwehr *n*

2015   MECHANICAL COVER
mechanical covering of a free water
surface to prevent evaporation
(e.g. styrofoam particles)
f   couverture *f* mécanique
d   mechanische Abdeckung *f*

2016   MEDIAN
value dividing frequency of variates
in two equal portions
f   médiane *f*
d   Zentralwert *m*; Medianwert *m*

2017   MEDICINAL SPRING
spring with healing properties

f source *f* thérapeutique
d Heilquelle *f*

2018 MEDIUM SAND
grain diameter 0.5 to 0.25 mm
(USBS)
f sable *m* moyen
d mittelkörniger Sand *m*

2019 MEINZER UNIT
measure of hydraulic conductivity
gpd per ft^2 under hydraulic
gradient of unity (USGS - adoption)
f Unité *f* Meinzer (USA)
d Meinzereinheit *f* (USA)

MELT, snow see 2584

2020 MELTING
passage from solid to liquid state
due to temperature increase
f fusion *f*
d Schmelzen *n*

2021 MELTING POINT
temperature at which a solid
substance is transformed into
its liquid state
f point *m* de fusion
d Schmelzpunkt *m*

2022 MELTWATER
water derived from melting of snow
pack or of glacier
f eau *f* de fonte
d Schmelzwässer *npl*

2023 MEMBRANE MODEL
simulation of piezometric surface
by rubber membrane
f modèle *m* à membrane élastique
d Membranmodell *n*

2024 MEMBRANE POTENTIAL
electrochemical potential arising
at a membrane that separates two
solutions of different concentrations
f potentiel *m* de membrane
d Membranpotential *n*

2025 MENISCUS
free surface or interface formed
by liquid in a capillary tube
f ménisque *m*
d Meniskus *m*

2026 MERCURY COLUMN
cylindrical bore in a manometer
filled with mercury
f colonne *f* de mercure
d Quecksilbersäule *f*

2027 MERCURY GAGE
f manomètre *m* à mercure
d Quecksilbermanometer *n*

2028 MERCURY INJECTION METHOD
measurement of porosity by
mercury injection into sample
f méthode *f* par injection de
mercure
d Quecksilberinjektionsverfahren *n*

2029 MESH
opening in sieve screen, number of
openings per inch
f maille *f*
d Masche *f*

2030 MESH SIZE
f ouverture *f* des mailles
d Maschenweite *f*

2031 MESOPHYTE
plant growing under intermediate
moisture conditions
f mésophyte *m*
d Mesophyte *f*

2032 MESOZOIC
geologic era preceding Cenozoic era
f Ère *f* Mésozoique
d Mesozoikum *n*

METAL, alkali see 53
-, monel see 2070

2033 METAMORPHIC WATER
water once associated with rocks
during their metamorphism
f eaux *fpl* régénérées (par le
métamorphisme)
d metamorphes Wasser *n*

2034 METEORIC WATER
water recently involved in atmospheric circulation
f eaux *fpl* météoriques
d meteorisches Wasser *n*

2035 METEOROLOGY
science dealing with all physical
phenomena occuring in the atmosph
f météorologie *f*
d Wetterkunde *f*; Meteorologie *f*

METER, current see 428
-, rotating see 2438
-, soil-moisture see 2592
-, water see 2942

2036 METERING PUMP
pump with a very constant and pre

volumetric delivery
f   pompe f doseuse
d   Dosierpumpe f

METHOD, backwashing see 130
-, basin see 158
-, ditch see 533
-, finite differences see 729
-, flooding see 746
-, gas expansion see 816
-, gravity see 884
-, mercury injection see 2028
-, numerical see 2117
-, recovery see 2369
-, tracer flow see 2815

2037 METHOD OF APPLICATION
f   méthode f d'application
d   Anwendungsmethode f

2038 METHOD OF IMAGES
theoretical treatment of hydraulic
effects of physical boundaries by
introduction of image sources or
sinks in a complex plane
f   principe m des images
d   Verfahren n imaginärer Ab-
    bildungen in der komplexen
    Ebene

2039 METHOD OF ITERATION
f   méthode f par itération
d   Iterationsmethode f

2040 MICA SCHIST
f   micaschiste m
d   Glimmerschiefer m

2041 MICROFISSURE
f   fissure f capillaire
d   Haarriss m

2042 MICROPORE
f   micropore m
d   Mikropore f; Kleinstpore f

2043 MICRO STRAINER
f   microtamis m
d   Feinsieb n; Mikrosieb n

2044 MIGRATION
movement of water or other fluid
in the geologic substratum, mostly
by natural causes
f   migration f
d   Wanderung f

MIGRATION, capillary see 241

MINE, surface see 2719

2045 MINE DRAINAGE
waters coming from or passing
through surface or subsurface mine
workings
f   eaux fpl de mine
d   Grubenwässer fpl; Grubenabfluss-
    wässer npl

MINE DRAINAGE, acid see 17

MINERAL, accessory see 10
-, clay see 301

2046 MINERAL OIL
f   huile f minérale
d   Mineralöl n

2047 MINERALS
mineral components of a rock,
often in macrocrystalline form
f   minéraux mpl
d   Mineralien npl

2048 MINERAL SPRING
spring water having high mineral
content
f   source f minérale
d   Mineralquelle f

2049 MINE WATER
water accumulating in a mine
f   eau f de mine
d   Grubenwasser n

2050 MINIMUM EVENT
f   événement m minimum
d   Minimalereignis n

2051 MINING OF GROUND WATER
permanent depletion of ground
water reserves
f   production f d'eau en excès
    des réserves d'exploitation
d   Grundwasserabbau m

2052 MIOCENE
geologic epoch in the Tertiary
period
f   Miocène m
d   Miozän n

2053 MISCIBLE
f   miscible
d   mischbar

2054 MISCIBLE DISPLACEMENT
displacement of a fluid saturating
a porous medium by another fluid
completely miscible with the first
f   déplacement m miscible

d Verdrängung *f* mit einem
Lösungsmittel

2055 MISSISSIPPIAN
geologic period of the Paleozoic era
f Carbonifère *m* inférieur
d Unterkarbon *n*

2056 MIXING LENGTH
length over which mixing occurs,
especially of momentum in
turbulent flow
f longueur *f* de mélange
d Mischlänge *f*

2057 MIXING RATIO
f coefficient *m* de mélange
d Mischverhältnis *n*

2058 MODE
most frequently occurring variate in
a frequency distribution
f mode *m*
d dichtester Wert *m*; häufigster
Wert *m*

2059 MODEL
simplified system bearing some
physical similiarity to prototype
f modèle *m*
d Modell *n*

MODEL, membrane see 2023
-, sand see 2463

2060 MODEL TECHNIQUE
method of solving complex physical
problems by using simplified
models
f technique *f* des modèles
d Modellverfahren *n*

2061 MODEL TEST
f essai sur modèle *m*
d Modellversuch *m*

MOISTURE, antecedent-soil
see 89

2062 MOISTURE ACCUMULATION
f accumulation *f* d'humidité
d Feuchteansammlung *f*

2063 MOISTURE CONTENT
gravimetric water vapor content
of air
f teneur *f* en humidité
d Feuchtigkeitsgehalt *m*

MOISTURE CONTENT, gravimetric
see 877

MOISTURE CONTENT, volumetric se
2909

2064 MOISTURE DEFICIENCY
water required to restore moisture
to field capacity in dessicated soil
f déficit *m* en humidité
d Bodenfeuchtedefizit *n*

2065 MOISTURE EQUIVALENT
soil moisture retained against a
gravitational force of 1000 g.
f équivalent *m* d'humidité
d Feuchteäquivalent *n*

MOISTURE POTENTIAL, see
capillary potential

2066 MOLECULAR ATTRACTION
f attraction *f* moléculaire
d molekulare Anziehungskraft *f*

2067 MOLECULAR DIFFUSION
f diffusion *f* moléculaire
d Molekulardiffusion *f*

2068 MOLLISOL
soil layer subject to annual
thawing and freezing, often mobile
when thawed
f mollisol *m*
d Fliesschicht *f*

2069 MOMENTUM
f moment *m* cinétique
d Impuls *m*

2070 MONEL METAL
f monel *m*
d Monel-Metall *n*

2071 MONOCLINE
tilted stratum
f monoclinal *m*
d Schichtflexur *f*; monoklinale
Flexur *f*

2072 MONOELECTRODE SONDE
f sonde *f* monoélectrode
d Einzelelektrodensonde *f*

2073 MONOMOLECULAR FILM
layer of monomolecular thickness
of a polar substance spread over a
free water surface to prevent
evaporation
f couche *f* monomoléculaire
d monomolekulare Schicht *f*

2074 MONTMORILLONITE
clay mineral containing MgO in its
structure

f   montmorillonite *m*
d   Montmorillonit *m*

2075   MOOR
       wet peat bog
       f   tourbière *f*
       d   Moor *n*

2076   MORAINE
       sand and rock material carried and
       deposited by glacier
       f   moraine *f*
       d   Moräne *f*

       MORAINE, lateral see 1135
       -, recessional see 2352
       -, terminal see 2759

2077   MORAINE DEPOSIT
       f   dépôt *m* morainique
       d   Moränenablagerung *f*;
           Moränenschutt *m*

2078   MORPHOMETRIC ANALYSIS
       geodetic and geometric description
       of basin and stream network
       f   analyse *f* hypsométrique
       d   morphometrische Analyse *f*

       MORTAR BED, see hardpan

2079   MOTHER LIQUID
       residual salt solution
       f   eau-mère *f*
       d   Mutterlauge *f*

       MOUNTAIN, table see 2743

2080   MOUNTAIN CHAIN
       series of mountains forming long
       stretched chain like line
       f   chaîne *f* de montagnes
       d   Gebirgskette *f*

       MOUTH, basin see 159

2081   MOUTH OF A WELL
       orifice at upper end of well
       f   tête *f* de puits; entrée *f* du puits
       d   Borhlochsmund *m*; Brunnenöffnung *f*

2082   MOVING ELECTRODE
       electrode travelling vertically in a
       well that is logged
       f   électrode *f* mobile
       d   bewegliche Elektrode *f*

2083   MUD
       water saturated fine clayey earth
       material

f   boue *f*
d   Schlamm *m*

MUD, drilling see 576

2084   MUD ADDITIVE
       various chemical additives to
       change the chemical and physical
       properties of a drilling mud
       f   additif *m* de boue de forage
       d   Spülungszusatz *m*

2085   MUD CIRCULATION
       complete circuit through which the
       drilling mud passes during operations
       f   circulation *f* de boue
       d   Spülungskreislauf *m*

2086   MUD COLUMN
       column of drilling mud in a well
       f   colonne *f* de boue
       d   Spülungssäule *f*

2087   MUD CRACK
       cracks appearing in drying mud
       surfaces due to shrinkage
       f   fente *f* de dessiccation
       d   Trockenriss *m*

2068   MUD FILTRATE
       part of drilling fluid that has
       passed the filter cake formed at
       the side wall of the well
       f   filtrat *m* de boue
       d   Spülungsfiltrat *n*

2089   MUDFLOW
       flow of water saturated rock debris
       f   coulée *f* de boue
       d   Schlammstrom *m*; Mure *f*

2090   MUD LOSS
       loss of drilling fluid into a thief
       zone or permeable layer of the
       formations penetrated
       f   perte *f* de boue
       d   Spülungsverlust *m*

2091   MUD PORT
       opening in drilling tool through
       which drilling mud extrudes
       f   sortie *f* de boue
       d   Spülungsauslass *m*

2092   MUD PUMP
       f   pompe *f* à boue
       d   Spülungspumpe *f*

2093   MULTIAQUIFER FORMATION
       formation with several aquifers

overlying each other
f   système *m* de couches
    aquifères superposées
d   Grundwasserstockwerk *n*

2094   MULTIAQUIFER WELL
       well completed and tapping several
       aquifers
f   puits *m* développé dans plusieurs
    nappes superposées
d   Brunnen *m* in einem Grundwasser-
    stockwerk

2095   MULTIPLE REFLECTIONS
       seismic waves that have been
       reflected at several bedding planes
f   réflexions *f pl* multiples
d   multiple Reflexionen *f pl*

2096   MYLONITE
       crushed and laminated rock
f   mylonite *m*
d   Mylonit *m*; Mahlgestein *n*

N

2097 NATIVE GROUND WATER
original ground water
f eau *f* phréatique indigène
d ursprüngliches Grundwasser *n*

2098 NATURAL DISCHARGE
discharge of water into surface
water bodies or springflow
f exutoire *m* naturel (de la nappe
   phréatique)
d natürlicher Grundwasseraustritt *m*

2099 NATURAL GAS
f gaz naturel *m*
d Erdgas *n*

2100 NATURAL LEVEE
river bank raised by river's own
depositions
f levée *f* de rive
d Uferdamm *m*

2101 NATURAL LOAD
sediment carried by stable stream
f charge *f* stabilisée
d natürliche Frachtung *f*

2102 NATURAL STREAM
f rivière *f* naturelle
d natürlicher Fluss *m*;
   ubeeinflusster Strom *m*

2103 NATURAL WATER
water with mineral content as
occurring under natural conditions
f eau *f* naturelle
d natürliches Wasser *n*

2104 NECK
volcanic pipe filled with lava
f diatrème *m*
d Diatrema *n*; Stielgang *m*

NET, flow see 760

2105 NET RADIATION
sum of incident and reflected sun
and sky shortwave radiation plus
incident and reflected atmospheric
long-wave radiation
f différence *f* du rayonnement;
   rayonnement *m* net
d Nettoeinstrahlung *f*

2106 NETWORK
f réseau *m*
d Netz *n*

NETWORK, drainage see 554
-, rain gage see 2332
-, resistance-capacity see 2395
-, synoptic see 2741

2107 NEUTRALITY POINT
separation point between acid and
basic solution with a pH of 7.0
f point *m* neutre
d Neutralitätspunkt *m*

2108 NEUTRON LOG
vertical recording of induced
neutron reactions, especially
sensitive to hydrogen content of
porous rocks
f diagraphie *f* neutron
d Neutronenlog *n*

2109 NEUTRON SOURCE
source producing fast neutrons
f source *f* de neutrons
d Neutronenquelle *f*

2110 NITROGEN
N_2
f azote *m*
d Stickstoff *m*

2111 NODE POINT
intersection point on grid
f noeud *m*
d Netzpunkt *m*; Knotenpunkt *m*

2112 NONRECORDING GAGE
standard rain gage (8 in standard in
USA)
f pluviomètre *m* standard
d Niederschlagsmesser *m*;
   Standardgerät *n*

2113 NORMAL CURVE
recording of a resistivity
measurement where spacing between
current and measuring electrode is
small compared to spacing of
measuring electrodes
f diagraphie *f* à espacement normal;
   normale *f*
d Normale *f*

2114 NORMAL DEPTH
depth at which uniform flow occurs
in open channel
f profondeur *f* normale
d normale Wassertiefe *f*

2115 NORMAL FAULT
fault showing relative downward
movement on the fault plane
f faille f directe
d normale Verwerfung f;
Abschiebung f

NUCLEUS, condensation see 341
-, hygroscopic see 991

2116 NUMBER OF REVOLUTIONS
f nombre m de tours
d Drehzahl f

2117 NUMERICAL METHOD
f méthode f numérique
d numerische (Lösungs-) Methode f

2118 NUMERICAL SOLUTION
f solution f numérique
d numerische Lösung f

O

2119 OASIS
limited area in the desert supplied
with water
f oasis *m*
d Oase *f*

2120 OBSEQUENT RIVER
river flowing in direction opposite
to that of the dip of underlying strata
f rivière *f* obséquente
d Stirnfluss *m*; obsequenter Fluss *m*

2121 OBSERVATION WELL
well drilled for the purpose of
making observations such as water
level or pressure recordings
f puits *m* d'observation; sonde *f*
d Beobachtungsbohrung *f*

2122 OBSIDIAN
volcanic glass
f obsidienne *f*
d Obsidian *m*

2123 OCEAN
body of salt water; sea
f océan *m*
d Ozean *m*; Weltmeer *n*

2124 OCEANIC WATER
sea water with a total salt content
of about 34,500 ppm.
f eau *f* de mer
d Meerwasser *n*

OIL, mineral see 2046

2125 OIL FIELD WATER
f eaux *f pl* des gisements
   pétrolifères
d Ölfeldwässer *n pl*

2126 OIL RESERVOIR
f gisement *m* de pétrole
d Erdöllagerstätte *f*

2127 OIL WELL
f puits *m* de pétrole
d Ölbohrung *f*

2128 OLIGOCENE
geologic epoch in the Tertiary
period
f Oligocène
d Oligozän *n*

2129 OLIVINE
peridot mineral occurring in ultra
basic igneous rocks
f olivine *f*
d Olivin *n*

2130 OOLITIC
of spherical or ovoidal shape
f oolithique
d oolithisch

2131 OPEN CHANNEL FLOW
f écoulement *m* dans un canal
d Fliessen *n* in offenem Kanal

2132 OPEN SYSTEM
system where matter and energy
may cross system boundary
f système *m* ouvert
d offenes System *n*

2133 OPERATING FLOOR
f plate-forme *f* de service
d Bedienungsbühne *f*; Werkbühne *f*

2134 OPTIMIZATION
f optimisation *f*
d Optimierung *f*

2135 ORDOVICIAN
geologic period of the Paleozoic era
f Ordovicien *m*
d Ordovizium *n*

2136 ORGANIC DEPOSIT
depostis of calcareous and siliceous
remains of animals
f dépôt *m* organogène
d organogene Ablagerung *f*

2137 ORGANIC MATTER CONTENT
f teneur *f* en matière organique
d organischer Inhalt *m*

2138 ORGANIC POLLUTION
contamination originating from
organic sources
f pollution *f* organique
d organische Verunreinigung *f*

2139 ORIENTATION
directional arrangement of
nonspherical grains in a sand
aggregate
f orientation *f*
d Orientierung *f*; richtungsmässige
   Anordung *f*

2140 ORIGINAL DIP
dip due to deposition of sediments
f pendage *m* original
d ursprüngliches Einfallen *n*

2141 ORIGINAL INTERSTICE
interstice formed during rock
formation stage
f porosité *f* d'interstice primaire;
interstice *m* de formation
d ursprünglicher Porenraum *m*

2142 OROGRAPHIC PRECIPITATION
precipitation due to mechanical
lifting of air over a ground relief
f précipitation *f* de relief
d orographischer Niederschlag *m*

2143 ORTHOGONALITY
f orthogonalité *f*
d Orthogonalität *f*

2144 OSMOTIC FORCE
f force *f* osmotique
d osmotische Kraft *m*

2145 OSMOTIC PRESSURE
f pression *f* osmotique
d osmotischer Druck *m*

2146 OUTCROP
open exposure of bedrock or
otherwise buried material
f affleurement *m*
d Aufschluss *m*

2147 OUTFLOW
f effluent *m*; écoulement *m*
d Ausfluss *m*; Abfluss *m*

2148 OUTPUT VOLTAGE
voltage available at terminals of a
power supply
f tension *f* aux bornes
d Klemmenspannung *f*

2149 OUTWASH
glacial drift deposited by meltwater
streams
f dépôt *m* d'eau de fonte
d Schmelzwasserablagerung *f*

2150 OUTWASH GRAVEL
glacial drift material deposited by
streams from glacier
f gravier *m* fluvioglaciaire
d ausgewaschener Kies *m*

2151 OUTWASH PLAIN
plain in front of glacier composed
of outwash material

f plaine *f* de lavage
d Sandrebene *f*

2152 OVEN-DRY
degree of dryness of porous sample
after drying in oven at specified
temperature
f sec à l'étuve
d ofentrocken

2153 OVERBANK AREA
area covered by flood waters
overtopping natural of artificial
river banks
f surface *f* du lit majeur
d Ausseruferungsgebiet *n*

2154 OVERBURDEN
total thickness of all strata overlying an aquifer or other formation
f couverture *f*; toit *m*
d Deckschichten *f pl*

2155 OVERBURDEN PRESSURE
pressure exerted by weight of the
overburden column
f pression *f* géostatique
d Überlagerungsdruck *m*

2156 OVERFLOW
f déversoir *m* de trop-plein
d Überlauf *m*

2157 OVERFLOW, TO
spill over containing walls
f déborder
d überlaufen

2158 OVERFLOW DAM
f barrage *m* déversoir
d Überflusswehr *n*

2159 OVERLAND FLOW
surface runoff flowing over land
surface towards channel
f ruissellement *m* de surface;
ruissellement *m* sur le terrain
d Oberflächenabfluss *m*

2160 OVERLOAD
load above the normal rating; exce
load still tolerable to system
f surcharge *f*
d Überlast *f*

2161 OVERPRESSURE
excess pressure
f pression *f* excédentaire
d Überdruck *m*

2162 OVERTHRUST
      upthrust fault with very low angle
      of dip and relatively large net
      displacement
      f   chevauchement *m*
      d   Überschiebung *f*

2163 OXYGEN
      O₂

f   oxygène *m*
d   Sauerstoff *m*

2164 OXYGEN DEMAND
      ability of substances to utilize
      dissolved oxygen in water
      f   demande *f* en oxygène
      d   Sauerstoffbedarf *m*

P

2165 PACKER
sealing device in well to separate
flow from different horizons
f packer *m*; garniture *f*;
étanchéité *m*
d Packer *m*; Dichtung *f*

2166 PACKING
three dimensional arrangement of
particles
f arrangement *m*; empilement *m*;
tassement *m*
d Packung *f*; Lagerung *f*;
Anordnung *f*

PACKING, grain see 862
-, gravel see 873
-, loosest see 1170
-, hightest see 2787

2167 PACKING GLAND
f presse-étoupe *m*
d Stopfbüchse *f*

2168 PALEOCENE
oldest geologic epoch in the
Tertiary period
f Paléocène *m*
d Paläozän *n*

2169 PALEOZOIC
geologic era preceding Mesozoic
era
f Ère *f* Paléozoïque
d Paläozoikum *n*

PAN, evaporation see 681
-, floating see 741
-, land see 1124
-, sunken see 2705

2170 PAN COEFFICIENT
coefficient to correlate high rate of
evaporation in pan to evaporation rate
from larger water bodies
f coefficient *m* de réduction d'un bac;
coefficient *m* du bac
d Kesselumrechnungskoeffizient *m*

2171 PARENT MATERIAL
material from which soil or sediment was formed
f roche *f* mère
d Ausgangsmaterial *n*

2172 PARTIALLY PENETRATED WELL
well not penetrating aquifer
completely to impervious bedrock
f puits *m* imparfait; puits *m*
incomplet
d unvollkommener Brunnen *m*

2173 PARTIAL PRESSURE OF VAPOR
f pression *f* partielle
d Partialdruck *m*

2174 PARTICLE
smallest individual constituent of
an aggregate
f particule *f*
d Teilchen *n*; Partikel *n*

PARTICLE, clay see 302
-, soil see 2595

2175 PARTING
separation of sedimentary rock
along the bedding planes
f délitement *m*
d Schichtfuge *f*

2176 PARTS PER MILLION (PPM)
weight per weight of solution;
expression of concentration
f parties *fpl* par million
d Teil *n* pro Million

2177 PATHOGENIC BACTERIA
disease inducing bacteria
f bactéries *fpl* pathogènes
d krankheitserregende Bakterien *f*

PATTERN, drainage see 555
-, pumping see 2306
-, storm intensity see 2655
-, trellis drainage see 2834

2178 PEAK
f pointe *f*; valeur *f* maximale
d Spitze *f*; Spitzenwert *m*;
Höchstwert *m*

2179 PEAK RUNOFF
f écoulement *m* de pointe
d Spitzenabfluss *m*

2180 PEAT
decomposed mainly vegetable
matter
f tourbe *f*
d Torf *m*

2181 PEBBLE
      smooth rounded stone
      f   caillou *m*; galet *m*
      d   Kieselstein *m*; Kiesel *m*

2182 PEDIMENT
      inclined erosion surface covered
      with thin fluvial deposits
      f   pédiment *m*
      d   Fussfläche *f*; Pediment *n*

2183 PELLICULAR WATER
      water adhering to soil particles
      by molecular forces
      f   eau *f* pelliculaire; eau *f* de
          tension superficielle
      d   Häutchenwasser *n*

2184 PENDULAR REGIME
      saturation regime where porous
      medium has lowest possible
      saturation in form of pendular rings
      at grain contacts
      f   régime *m* des eaux cunéiformes
      d   Porenwinkelwasserregime *n*;
          Pendulärregime *n*

2185 PENEPLAIN
      degradation surface without relief
      f   pénéplaine *f*
      d   Fastebene *f*; Rumpfebene *f*

2186 PENETRABLE
      f   pénétrable
      d   durchdringbar; durchlässig

      PENETRATION, complete .... of
      well see 329

2187 PENETRATION RATE
      f   vitesse *f* d'avancement
      d   Vorschubgeschwindigkeit *f*;
          Bohrfortschritt *m*

2188 PENNSYLVANIAN
      geologic period of the Paleozoic era
      f   Carbonifère *m* supérieur
      d   Oberkarbon *n*

2189 PEN TRACE
      ink, magnetic, or photographic line
      traced on drum of a recording gage
      or meter
      f   trace *f* du stylet
      d   Schreibspur *f*

190   PERCHED GROUNDWATER
      isolated continuous body of water
      suspended above water table
      f   nappe *f* perchée
      d   schwebendes Grundwasser *n*

2191 PERCHED WATER TABLE
      free surface of a continuous body
      of water suspended above main
      water table
      f   surface *f* d'une nappe perchée
      d   schwebender Grundwasserspiegel *m*

2192 PERCOLATE
      to flow through saturated void space
      f   percoler
      d   durchsickern; durchströmen

2193 PERCOLATION
      movement of water through saturated
      interior pore space
      f   percolation *f*
      d   Sickerströmung *f*; Filterströmung *f*

2194 PERCUSSION DRILLING
      f   forage *m* par battage
      d   Schlagbohrverfahren *n*

2195 PERENNIAL SPRING
      spring discharging throughout the
      year
      f   source *f* pérenne
      d   Dauerquelle *f*; perennierende
          Quelle *f*

2196 PERENNIAL STREAMS
      stream flowing above surface all
      the time
      f   rivière *f* pérenne
      d   perennierender Fluss *m*

2197 PERENNIAL YIELD
      sustained yield
      f   débit *m* d'écoulement pérenne
      d   Dauerspende *f*

2198 PERFORATION
      holes or openings in well casing to
      permit water inflow into well
      f   perforation *f*
      d   Perforation *f*; Durchlöcherung *f*

      PERIMETER, basin see 160
      -, wetted see 3010

2199 PERIOD
      subdivision of an era in the geologic
      time scale
      f   période *f*
      d   Periode *f*

      PERIOD, wetting see 3011

2200 PERMAFROST
      ground perennially below the freezing
      temperature
      f   pergelisol *m*
      d   Dauerfrost *m*; Permafrost *m*; Gefrornis

2201 PERMAFROST TABLE
      upper limit of permafrost
      f   limite *f* supérieure du pergelisol
      d   obere Permafrostgrenze *f*

2202 PERMANENT HARDNESS
      noncarbonate hardness
      f   dureté *f* permanente; dureté *f*
          non-carbonatée
      d   bleibende Härte *f*; permanente
          Härte *f*

2203 PERMANENT LOAD
      f   charge *f* permanente
      d   Dauerlast *f*; Nennlast *f*

2204 PERMANENT WELL
      well completely equipped and
      developed for a long productive life
      (as opposed to an observation or
      exploratory well)
      f   puits *m* permanent
      d   endgültige Bohrung *f*

2205 PERMANENT WILTING POINT
      saturation at which permanent
      wilting occurs
      f   point *m* de flétrissure permanente
      d   permanenter Welkepunkt *m*

      PERMEABILITY, effective see 622
      -, intrinsic see 1071
      -, relative see 2384
      -, transverse see 2829

2206 PERMEABILITY BARRIER
      geologic or petrographic feature in
      a bed obstructing free flow
      f   barrière *f* de perméabilité
      d   Permeabilitätsbarriere *f*

2207 PERMEABILITY TENSOR
      permeability in an anisotropic
      medium
      f   tenseur *m* de perméabilité
      d   Permeabilitätstensor *m*

2208 PERMEAMETER
      device to measure permeability
      f   perméamètre *m*
      d   Permeameter *n*; Vorrichtung *f*
          zur Durchlässigkeitsmessung

2209 PERMIAN
      most recent geologic period of the
      Paleozoic era
      f   Permien *m*
      d   Perm *n*

2210 PERMISSIBLE LOAD
      f   charge *f* admissible
      d   zulässige Belastung *f*

2211 PERVIOUS
      permitting fluids to pass
      f   perméable
      d   durchlässig

2212 PETROGRAPHY
      science of describing and
      identifying rocks
      f   pétrographie *f*
      d   Petrographie *f*; Gesteinskunde *f*

2213 PHOTOGEOLOGY
      interpretation of aerial photographs
      for geological purposes
      f   photogéologie *f*
      d   Photogeologie *f*

2214 PHOTOGRAMMETRY
      preparation of maps and measureme
      from (stereoscopic) aerial photo-
      graphs
      f   photogrammétrie *f*
      d   Photogrammetrie *f*

2215 PHOTOMULTIPLIER
      f   photomultiplicateur *m*
      d   Photoelektronenverstärkerröhre

2216 PHREATIC DECLINE
      downward movement of water table
      f   abaissement *m* phréatique
      d   Grundwasserspiegelabfall *m*

2217 PHREATIC FLUCTUATION
      fluctuation of the water table
      f   fluctuation *f* phréatique
      d   Schwankung *f* des Grundwasser-
          spiegels

2218 PHREATIC RISE
      upward movement of water table
      f   remontée *f* phréatique
      d   Grundwasserspiegelanstieg *m*

2219 PHREATIC SURFACE
      free water surface at atmospheric
      pressure
      f   surface *f* de la nappe phréatiqu
      d   Grundwasseroberfläche *f*

2220 PHREATIC WATER
      see ground water

2221 PHREATIC ZONE
      zone in soil profile saturated with
      ground water; a zone of saturation
      f   zone *f* de l'eau soutenue;
          zone *f* phréatique
      d   Grundwasserzone *f*

2222 PHREATOPHYTE
      desert plants with deeply penetrat

roots reaching the water table,
growing mainly along stream course
(word proposed by E.O. Meinzer)
f   phréatophythe *m*
d   Phreatophyte *f*

2223   pH VALUE
negative exponent of hydrogen ion
concentration
f   valeur *f* du pH
d   pH-Wert *m*; Wasserstoff
exponent *m*

2224   PHYLLITE
metamorphic argillaceous rock
f   phyllade *m*
d   Phyllit *m*

2225   PHYSICAL ANALYSIS
f   analyse *f* physique
d   physikalische Untersuchung *f*

2226   PHYSIOGRAPHY
science of the origin and evolution
of land forms
f   physiographie *f*
d   Physiographie *f*

2227   PHYTOMETER
device to measure transpiration of
plants embedded in soil
f   phytomètre *m*
d   Pflanzenverdunstungsmesser *m*

2228   PIEDMONT PLAIN
plain extending outwards from the
base of a mountain system
f   plaine *f* de piémont
d   Bergfussebene *f*

2229   PIEZOMETER
pressure reading and measuring
instrument
f   piézomètre *m*
d   Druckmesser *m*

2230   PIEZOMETRIC HEAD
sum of pressure and elevation head
f   hauteur *f* piézométrique;
énergie *f* potentielle
d   piezometrische Druckhöhe *f*

2231   PIEZOMETRIC POTENTIAL
piezometric head
f   potentiel *m* piézométrique
d   Druckpotential *n*

2232   PIEZOMETRIC SURFACE
defined by elevation to which water
will rise in artesian wells or wells

penetrating confined aquifers,
determined by water pressure and
elevation of aquifer
f   surface *f* piézométrique
d   Druckfläche *f*; piezometrisches
Niveau *n*

2233   PILLOW LAVA
lava showing structure resembling
pillows
f   lave *m* en coussins
d   Kissenlava *f*

2234   PILOT BIT
f   outil-pilote *m*
d   Vorbohrmeissel *m*

2235   PINGO;
HYDROLACCOLITH
see hydrolaccolith
f   laccolith *m* de glace
d   Eislakkolith *m*

2236   PIPE
closed tubular conduit for fluid
transport
f   tuyeau *m*; tubage *m*
d   Rohr *n*

PIPE, discharge see 518
-, riser see 2414
-, screen see 2486
-, seamless see 2489
-, slotted see 2574
-, stove see 2656
-, tile see 2788
-, water see 2946

2237   PIPE CASING
lining of a well in form of tubular
steel or cast iron pipe
f   tubage *m*
d   Verrohrung *f*

2238   PIPE COUPLING
f   manchon *m* de tubage
d   Rohrverbinder *m*

2239   PIPE LINE
f   conduit *m*; pipeline *m*
d   Pipeline *f*; Fernleitung *f*

PIPE LINE, gas see 819

2240   PIPE MANIFOLD
f   collecteur *m*
d   Verteilerrohr *n*

2241   PIPE WRENCH
f   clé *f* à tubes
d   Rohrzange *f*

2242 PIT
f fosse *f*
d Grube *f*

PIT, gravel see 874
-, recharge see 2359
-, settling see 2517
-, slush see 2577
-, test see 2764
-, well see 2997

2243 PITCHER PUMP
a type of piston pump
f pompe *f* à plongeur
d Tauchkolbenpumpe *f*

2244 PITOT TUBE
device to measure flow velocity
through pressure differences
f tube *m* de Pitot
d Staudruckmesser *m*;
   Pitot'sche Röhre *f*

PLAIN, alluvial see 60
-, coastal see 315
-, flood see 748
-, outwash see 2151
-, piedmont see 2228

PLANE, bedding see 167
-, contact see 366
-, datum see 442
-, fault see 708
-, hodograph see 934
-, joint see 1101

2245 PLANIMETER
instrument for the automatic
determination of irregular areas on
a map
f planimètre *m*
d Planimeter *n*

PLATE, base see 154
-, slotted see 2575

2246 PLATEAU
elevated level land surface
f plateau *m*
d Plateau *n*; Hochebene *f*

PLATEAU, lava flow see 1139

2247 PLATY
f en forme de plaquette
d plättchenförmig

2248 PLEISTOCENE
geologic epoch in the Quaternary
period

f Pléistocène *m*
d Pleistozän *n*

2249 PLIOCENE
most recent geologic epoch in the
Tertiary period
f Pliocène *m*
d Pliozän *n*

2250 PLUGGING AGENT
mud additive that seals off a very
permeable layer by clogging of the
borehole walls
f colmatant *m*
d Dichtungsmittel *n*

2251 PLUNGER PUMP
f pompe *f* à piston; pompe *f* à
   plongeur
d Kolbenpumpe *f*; Tauchkolbenpumpe *f*

2252 PLUTONIC WATER
water in or derived from magna at
considerable depth
f eaux *f pl* plutoniques
d plutonisches Wasser *n*

2253 POCKET STORAGE
water storage in depressions on the
land surface
f emmagasinement *m* dans les
   dépressions du sol
d Wasserspeicherung *f* an der
   Bodenoberfläche

2254 PODSOL
light colored soil (forest regions)
f podzol *m*
d Podsolboden *m*

POINT, concentration see 337
-, drive see 592
-, freezing see 787
-, match see 1197
-, melting see 2021
-, neutrality see 2107
-, node see 2111
-, reference see 2376
-, saturation see 2472
-, shock see 2536
-, shot see 2540
-, stagnation see 2636
-, triple see 2842
-, wilting see 3016

2255 POINT-BAR DEPOSIT
sedimentation on inside of meande'
loop
f banc *m* de sable à l'intérieur de
   boucle

d Sandbank *f* am Gleithang;
Anlandung *f*

2256 POINT OF INFLECTION
point where curve changes slope
f point *m* d'inflexion
d Wendepunkt *m*

2257 POINT OF RISE
f point *m* de montée
d Anstiegspunkt *m*

2258 POISE
measure of viscosity
f poise *f*
d Poise *n*

2259 POLARIZATION
migration and separation of ions to
the electrodes in a direct current
electrolyte process giving rise to
higher overall resistance
f polarisation *f*
d Polarisierung *f*

2260 POLLUTANT
substance causing pollution
f matière *f* polluante
d Verunreinigung *f*;
Schmutzstoff *m*

2261 POLLUTED WATER
water containing sewage or other
contaminants
f eaux *f pl* polluées
d verunreinigtes Wasser *n*;
Abwasser *n*; Schmutzwasser *n*

2262 POLLUTION
contamination of the environment
with undesirable or obnoxious
substances
f pollution *f*
d Verschmutzung *f*;
Verunreinigung *f*

POLLUTION, organic see 2138

2263 POLLUTION ABATEMENT
all measures taken to prevent or to
protect against pollution
f protection *f* contre la pollution
d Gewässerschutz *m*

2264 POND
small body of surface water
f étang *m*
d Teich *m*

2265 PONDED WATER
water held in depression by a barrier

f eaux *f pl* retenues
d eingedämmtes Wasser *n*

2266 PORE
small void space in rock or
unconsolidated aggregate of soil
particles
f pore *m*
d Pore *f*; Hohlraum *m*

2267 PORE ENTRY RADIUS
radius of flow channel at pore entry,
smaller than average pore radius
f rayon *m* d'entrée de pore;
rayon *m* d'étranglement de pore
d Poreneintrittsradius *m*

2268 PORE PRESSURE
pressure of water in pores of
saturated medium
f pression *f* de pore
d Porendruck *m*; Porenwasserdruck *m*

2269 PORE SPACE
space occupied by voids, containing
gases or liquids, in a rock sample
f volume *m* des pores
d Porenraum *m*

PORE SPACE, vugular see 2910

2270 POROSIMETER
device to measure porosity
f porosimètre *m*
d Porosimeter *n*

2271 POROSITY
ratio of void volume to bulk volume
of rock sample
f porosité *f*
d Porosität *f*; Porengehalt *m*

POROSITY, absolute see 6
-, effective see 623, 624
-, practical see 623
-, secondary see 2493

2272 POROUS MEDIUM
any medium containing interdispersed
void space
f milieu *m* poreux
d poröses Medium *n*

2273 POTABILITY
f potabilité *f*
d Trinkbarkeit *f*

2274 POTABLE WATER
f eau *f* potable
d Trinkwasser *n*

2275 POTAMOLOGY
study of streams
f potamologie *f*
d Potamologie *f*; Flusskunde *f*

2276 POTASSIUM
K
f potasse *m*
d Kalium *n*

2277 POTENTIAL
f potentiel *m*
d Potential *n*

POTENTIAL, contact see 367
-, electrochemical see 635
-, force see 775
-, membrane see 2024
-, junction see 1102
-, piezometric see 2231
-, redox see 2371
-, spontaneous see 2626
-, streaming see 2668
-, velocity see 2891
-, zeta see 3030

2278 POTENTIAL ELECTRODE
f électrode *f* de potentiel
d Potentialelektrode *f*;
Messelektrode *f*

2279 POTENTIAL EVAPOTRANSPIRATION
evapotranspiration occurring under
adequate soil-moisture supply at all
times for given temperature and
humidity conditions
f évapotranspiration *f* potentielle
d mögliche Evapotranspiration *f*;
potentielle Evapotranspiration *f*

2280 POTENTIAL FLOW
irrotational flow occurring in a
conservative force field or
potential field
f écoulement *m* potentiel
d Potentialströmung *f*

2281 POTENTIOMETER
instrument to measure voltage
differences
f potentiomètre *m*
d Potentiometer *n*; Spannungsmesser *m*

2282 POTHOLE
hole formed by the erosive action
of whirling water
f marmite *f* torrentielle
d Kolk *m*; Erosionskessel *m*

2283 PRACTICAL POROSITY
see effective porosity

2284 PRE-CAMBIAN
geologic era preceding Cambrain
period
f Antécambrien *m*
d Präkambrium *n*

2285 PRECIPITATION
water precipitating in liquid or solid
form from atmosphere
f précipitation *m*
d Niederschlag *m*

PRECIPITATION, accumulated
see 13
-, channel see 279
-, convective see 379
-, cyclonic see 434
-, effective see 625
-, orographic see 2142

2286 PRECIPITATION-EVAPORATION
RATIO
f rapport *m* précipitation-évaporatio
d Niederschlags-Verdunstungs-
verhältnis *n*

2287 PRECIPITATION EXCESS
part of precipitation contributing
directly to runoff
f précipitation *f* excédentaire
d Niederschlagsüberschuss *m*

2288 PRECIPITATION GAGE
instrument to measure amount of
precipitation per unit area
f appareil *m* de mesure de la
précipitation
d Niederschlagsmesser *m*

PRECIPITATION INDEX,
antecedent see 88

2289 PRESSURE
f pression *f*
d Druck *m*

PRESSURE, absolute see 7
-, air see 44
-, barometric see 142
-, differential see 501
-, discharge see 519
-, flowing see 757
-, gage see 804
-, hydrostatic see 986
-, initial see 1035
-, osmotic see 2145
-, overburden see 2155

-, pore see 2268
-, saturation see 2473
-, working see 3023

2290 PRESSURE BUILDUP CURVE
  f   courbe *f* de remontée de
      pression
  d   Druckaufbaukurve *f*

2291 PRESSURE CELL
  pressure measuring and
  transducing device
  f   cellule *f* piézométrique
  d   Druckdose *f*

2292 PRESSURE DROP
  pressure difference occurring
  between two points along a stream
  line in a flow system
  f   chute *f* de pression
  d   Druckabfall *m*; Druckverlust *m*

2293 PRESSURE HEAD
  f   énergie *f* de pression
  d   Druckhöhe *f*

  PRESSURE OF VAPOR, partial
  see 2173

2294 PRESSURE SURGE
  f   à-coup *m* de pression
  d   Druckstoss *m*

2295 PRESSURE TRANSMITTER
  f   transducteur *m* de pression
  d   Druckgeber *m*

2296 PRISM STORAGE
  storage of water in river channel
  or reservoir in prism above
  original water level
  f   emmagasinement *m* prismatique
  d   prismatisch gespeichertes Fall-
      wasser *n*

2297 PROBE
  sensing instrument to take
  measurements at the interior of
  a relatively unaccessible system
  f   sonde *f*
  d   Sonde *f*

  PROCESS, congealing see 354
  -, erosional see 669
  -, geomorphic see 836
  -, transportational see 2828

  PROFILE, flood see 749
  -, hydraulic see 957
  -, seismic see 2503

-, soil see 2596
-, stream see 2671
-, zonal soil see 3032

2298 PROTECTIVE CASING
  f   tubage *m* de protection
  d   Schutzverrohrung *f*

2299 PSYCHROMETER
  apparatus to measure relative
  humidity indirectly
  f   psychromètre *m*
  d   Psychrometer *n*

2300 PUDDLE
  water collecting in very small
  surface depressions
  f   flaque *f* d'eau
  d   Pfütze *f*

2301 PULLEY
  f   moufle *m*
  d   Flaschenzugblock *m*

2302 PULSE GENERATOR
  f   générateur *m* de pulsations
  d   Pulsgenerator *m*

2303 PUMICE
  glassy, very porous lava
  f   pierre *f* ponce
  d   Bimsstein *m*

  PUMP, centrifugal see 273
  -, deep well turbine see 449
  -, displacement see 526
  -, double acting see 540
  -, gear see 823
  -, jet see 1097
  -, metering see 2036
  -, mud see 2092
  -, pitcher see 2243
  -, plunger see 2251
  -, sand see 2464
  -, submersible see 2684
  -, suction see 2698

  PUMPAGE, water see 2947

2304 PUMP DISCHARGE
  f   refoulement *m* de la pompe
  d   Pumpenförderung *f*

2305 PUMP HOUSE
  f   abri *m* des pompes
  d   Pumpenkammer *f*

2306 PUMPING PATTERN
  arrangement of pumping wells
  f   disposition *f* des puits de pompag
  d   Entnahmeanordnung *f*

2307   PUMPING STATION
       f   station f de pompage
       d   Pumpstation f

2308   PUMPING TEST
       test to determine aquifer
       characteristics by pumping well
       and plotting drawdown curves
       f   essai m de pompage; essai m de
           puits
       d   Pumpversuch m

2309   PUMPING UNIT
       f   groupe m de pompes
       d   Pumpanlage f

2310   PUMP LINER
       liner of pump cylinder
       f   chemise f de pompe
       d   Pumpenauskleidung f

2311   PYCNOMETER
       bottle with accurately determined
       volume for density determinations
       f   pycnomètre m

       d   Pyknometer n

2312   PYRITE
       mineral FeS_2, sometimes source
       of sulfuric contaminations
       f   pyrite m
       d   Schwefelkies m; Pyrit m

2313   PYROCLASTIC BLOCK
       detrital volcanic block
       f   bloc m pyroclastique
       d   pyroklastischer Block m

2314   PYROCLASTIC FLOW
       dense, viscous lavaflow containing
       clastic material; ignimbrite
       f   tuf m soudé; ignimbrite m
       d   geschweisster Tuff m;
           Schmelztuff m

2315   PYROXENE
       mineral group of common rock-
       forming constituents
       f   pyroxène m
       d   Pyroxen n

Q

2316 QUAGMIRE
wet and unstable land area
f   bourbe *f*
d   Morast *m*

2317 QUARTERNARY
geologic period of the Cenozoic era
f   Ère *f* Quaternaire
d   Quartär *n*

2318 QUARTZ
crystal form of SiO_2

f   quartz *m*
d   Quarz *m*

2319 QUICKSAND
f   sable *m* mouvant
d   Schwimmsand *m*

2320 QUIET REACH
reach of river with no features
disturbing flow pattern
f   section *f* tranquille
d   ruhige Strecke *f*

R

2321 RADIAL FLOW
radial flow into or out of a well
under ideal circular boundary
conditions
f écoulement *m* radial circulaire
d radialer Fluss *m*

2322 RADIOACTIVE CONTAMINATION
f contamination *f* radioactive
d Strahlenverseuchung *f*

2323 RADIOACTIVE TRACER
tracer used in hydrological velocity
determinations
f traceur *m* radioactif
d radioaktive Markierung *f*;
radioaktiver Tracer *m*

2324 RADIOACTIVITY LOG
log measuring radioactivity in a
borehole
f diagraphie *f* de radioactivité
d Aufnahme *f* der Radioaktivität

2325 RADIOISOTOPE
f radio-isotope *m*; isotope *m*
radioactif
d radioaktives Isotop *n*

RADIUS, drainage see 556
-, hydrualic see 958
-, pore entry see 2267

2326 RADIUS OF INFLUENCE
radial distance to points around well
affected by pumping
f rayon *m* d'appel; rayon *m* d'action
d Absenkungsradius *m*

2327 RAIN
liquid precipitation of atmospheric
water in form of drops and droplets
f pluie *f*
d Regen *m*

RAINFALL, effective see 626

2328 RAIN FALL EXCESS
portion of rainfall contributing
directly to runoff
f pluie *f* excédentaire
d Regenüberschuss *m*

2329 RAINFALL INTENSITY
volume or depth of rainfall per unit
time

f intensité *f* de la pluie
d Regenintensität *f*; Regenstärke *f*

2330 RAINFALL SIMULA TOR
laboratory device to simulate
rainstorms
f simulateur *m* pluviométrique
d Regensimulator *m*; Berieselungs-
anlage *f*

2331 RAIN GAGE
instrument to measure height of
rainfall
f pluviomètre *m*
d Regenmesser *m*

2332 RAIN GAGE NETWORK
areal distribution of rain gages
f réseau *m* pluviométrique
d Niederschlagsbeobachtungsnetz *n*

2333 RAIN INTENSITY
intensity of rain fall expressed in
depth per time (inch hour)
f intensité *f* de pluie
d Regenintensität *f*

2334 RANDOM DISTRIBUTION
f distribution *f* aléatoire
d Zufallsverteilung *f*

2335 RANDOM SAMPLE
f échantillon *m* instantané
d Stichprobe *f*

2336 RAPID
stream section with notably higher
flow velocity than in adjoining parts
f rapide *m*
d Stromschnelle *f*

2337 RAPID FLOW
open channel flow with Froude
number greater than unity
f débit *m* rapide; écoulement *m*
rapide
d Schiessen *n*

RATE, drilling see 581
-, flow see 761
-, lapse see 1129
-, penetration see 2187
-, seepage see 2500
-, swelling see 2736

2338 RATE OF DRAFT
rate at which water is required
for use; demand
f débit *m* d'écoulement
d Verbrauchsrate *f*

2339 RATE OF DRYING
f taux *m* de dessèchement
d Trocknungsrate *f*

2340 RATE OF INFILTRATION
maximum rate at which soil can
absorb water
f capacité *f* d'infiltration
d Eindringungsrate *f*

2341 RATE OF PRODUCTION
f taux *m* de production
d Förderrate *f*

2342 RATING CURVE
graphic relationship of stage to
discharge
f courbe *f* de tarage
d Abflusskurve *f*

RATIO, bifurcation see 178
-, drainage see 557
-, mixing see 2057
-, precipitation-evaporation see
2286
-, relief see 2387
-, transpiration see 2827
-, void see 2899

2343 RATIONAL FORMULA
equation relating runoff intensity
and area to a runoff coefficient
f équation *f* rationelle
d rationale Abflussformel *f*

2344 RAVINE
small erosional depression
f ravin *m*
d Tobel *m*; kleine Schlucht *f*

2345 RAW WATER
untreated water
f eaux *f pl* non-traitées
d unbehandeltes Wasser *n*;
Rohwasser *n*

REACH, quiet see 2320

2346 REAMED WELL
well that has been enlargened by
reaming the original hole
f puits *m* alésé; puits *m* élargi
d nachgeräumter Brunnen *f*;
erweiterte Bohrung *f*

2347 REAMER
cutting tool to enlargen the diameter
of existing holes
f outil *m* aléseur
d Nachschneider *m*; Räumer *m*

2348 REAMING OF A SLIM HOLE
enlarging of a test hole to a pumping
or permanent well
f élargissement *m* d'une sonde à
faible diamètre
d Ausräumen *n* einer kleinen
Bohrung; Erweiterungsbohrung *f*

2349 RECEIVER
part of a remote measuring system
receiving incoming data or impulses
f récepteur *m*
d Empfänger *m*

2350 RECEIVING SURFACE
surface receiving precipitation
or radiation
f surface *f* de réception
d Auffangfläche *f*

2351 RECEIVING WATER COURSE
f cours *m* d'eau récepteur
d Vorfluter *m*

RECESSION, groundwater see 907

2352 RECESSIONAL MORAINE
moraine deposited by a retreating
glacier
f moraine *f* de retrait
d Rückzugsmoräne *f*

2353 RECESSION CONSTANT
f constante *f* de récession
d Rückgangskonstante *f*

2354 RECESSION CURVE
falling limb of hydrograph curve
f courbe *f* de décrue; courbe *f*
de tarissement
d abfallender Kurvenast *m* der
Ganglinie; Rückgangskurve *f*

2355 RECESSION FLOW
flow after rainfall stops
f écoulement *m* en décrue
d Abflussrückgang *m*

2356 RECESSION SEGMENT
part of hydrograph representing
withdrawal of water from storage
f segment *m* de tarissement
d Trockenwetterlinie *f*

2357 RECHARGE
artificial replenishment of a depleted
aquifer by injection or infiltration
of water from the surface
f recharge *f*; alimentation *f*
artificielle
d künstliche Grundwasseranreicherung *f*; Wiederauffüllung *f*

RECHARGE, artificial see 117
-, induced see 1016

2358 RECHARGE LINE
recharge wells arranged in linear
fashion to approximate line source
f ligne *f* de recharge
d Versickerungsbrunnenkette *f*

2359 RECHARGE PIT
large diameter well or shaft for
recharge under gravity
f fossé *m* de recharge
d Versickerungschacht *m*; Senk-
schacht *m*; Sickerschacht *m*

2360 RECHARGE WATER
water used for replenishment
f eaux *f pl* de recharge
d künstliches Grundwasser *n*

2361 RECHARGE WELL;
DIFFUSION WELL; INVERTED
WELL
well into which recharge water
is introduced
f puits *m* de recharge
d Versickerungsbrunnen *m*;
Senkbrunnen *m*

2362 RECIPIENT
vessel receiving liquids in volume
measurements
f récipient *m*
d Auffanggefäss *n*

2363 RECLAMATION
improve land use, eliminate ill
effects for this purpose
f récupération *f*
d Rückgewinnung *f*; Wieder-
herstellung *f*; Melioration *f*

RECLAMATION, water see 2949

RECORD, stage see 2635
-, well see 2999

2364 RECORDER
instrument continuously or intermittently recording measurements

f enregistreur *m*
d Schreiber *m*; Registriergerät *n*

RECORDER, water-stage see 2959

2365 RECORDING DRUM
f tambour *m* enregistreur
d Registriertrommel *f*;
Registrierwalze *f*

2366 RECORDING GAGE
f pluviographe *m*
d Niederschlagsschreiber *m*;
Schreibregenmesser *m*

2367 RECORDING OSCILLOGRAPH
f oscillographe *m* enregistreur
d Oszillograph *m*

2368 RECOVERY
f récupération *f*
d Ausbeute *f*

2369 RECOVERY METHOD
pumping test in which both drawdown
and recovery of head after pumping
has stopped are observed in the
same well
f méthode *f* par remontée
d Druckaufbauverfahren *n*

2370 RECRYSTALLIZATION
new formation of crystals from
solid rock material
f recristallisation *f*
d Rekristallisation *f*

2371 REDOX POTENTIAL (Eh)
oxidation-reduction potential
f potentiel *m* redox
d Redoxpotential *n*

2372 REDUCER
pipe or casing connector reducing
the diameter
f réducteur *m*
d Reduzierstück *n*

2373 REDUCING JOINT
f raccord *m* réducteur
d Reduzierverbindung *f*

2374 REDUCTION
mechanical device to reduce speed
or length of a trace
f démultiplication *f*
d Untersetzung *f*

REDUCTION, evaporation see 682
-, surface area see 2712

2375 REEF
dissected ridge of rocks totally or
partially submerged in sea water,
often of organic origin
f récif *m*
d Riff *n*

2376 REFERENCE POINT
f point *m* de référence
d Bezugspunkt *m*

2377 REGELATION
melting of ice under pressure and
subsequent freezing
f regelation *f*
d Regelation *f*

REGIME, fumicular see 801
-, pendular see 2184
-, saturation see 2474

REGIMEN, flow see 762

2378 REGION OF DISPERSED WATER
diffuse interface between fresh-
water and sea water caused by
mixing in a coastal aquifer
f zone *f* de transition saumâtre
d Brackwasserzone *f* im
   Grundwasserleiter

2379 REGOSOL
dry sandy soil
f sol *m* sablonneux
d Sandboden *m*

2380 REGRESSION LINE
curve fitted to all mean values of
one variable
f courbe *f* de régression
d Ausgleichskurve *f*

2381 REGULATION RESERVOIR
f réservoir *m* de compensation
d Ausgleichbehälter *m*

2382 REJUVENATION
occurrence of young morphologic
forms in a mature relief
f rajeunissement *m*
d Verjüngung *f*

2383 RELATIVE HUMIDITY OF
ATMOSPHERE
ratio of absolute humidity to
maximum possible saturation at
given conditions
f humidité *f* relative
d relative Luftfeuchte *f*

2384 RELATIVE PERMEABILITY
ratio of permeability of one
immiscible phase to intrinsic
permeability in multiphase flow
f perméabilité *f* relative
d relative Durchlässigkeit *f*;
   relative Permeabilität *f*

2385 RELIEF
elevation differences in topography
of a land surface
f relief *m*
d Relief *n*

RELIEF, maximum basin see 1198

2386 RELIEF INTENSITY
average altitude difference between
the highest point of a basin and the
valley bottom
f vigueur *f* du relief
d Reliefenergie *f*

2387 RELIEF RATIO
ratio of basin relief to horizontal
distance along which it is measured
f indice *m* du relief
d Reliefenergie *f*; Geländeneigung *f*

2388 REPLENISHMENT
restoration of water in depleted
aquifer
f alimentation *f*; ralimentation *f*
d Anreicherung *f*

2389 RESEQUENT RIVER
river flowing according to consequent
drainage pattern, however, at lower
level than original slope
f rivière *f* réséquente
d resequenter Fluss *m*

2390 RESERVOIR
a) recipient for the collection of
   small amount of liquid
b) surface water impoundment
f réservoir *m*
d a) Sammelbehälter *m*
   b) Stausee *m*; Speichersee *m*

RESERVOIR, groundwater see 909
-, oil see 2126
-, regulation see 2381

2391 RESERVOIR EVAPORATION
evaporation from the free surface
of impounded water bodies
f évaporation *f* sur les retenues
d Seeverdunstung *f*;
   Stauseeverdunstung *f*

2392 RESERVOIR LAKE
lake obtained by the impoundment
of water for storage purposes
f lac *m* de barrage
d Stausee *m*

2393 RESIDUAL DRAWDOWN
drawdown measured after stopping
of pumping in a single well test
f rabattement *m* résiduel
d Restabsenkung *f*

2394 RESIDUE
solids remaining after evaporation
f résidu *m* après évaporation;
résidu *m*
d Verdunstungsrückstand *m*;
Rückstand *m*; Abdampfrück-
stand *m*; Rest *m*

RESIDUE, dry see 604

RESISTANCE, acoustic see 19
-, flow see 763
-, wear see 2973

2395 RESISTANCE-CAPACITY NETWORK
electrical analog model simulating
viscous flow by flow of electricity
through resistors and capacitors
f réseau *m* à résistances -
capacitances
d Widerstands-Kapazitätsnetz *n*

2396 RESISTANCE THERMOMETER
thermometer based on the principle
that the resistivity of a platinum
wire is proportional to its temperature
f thermomètre *m* à résistance
d Widerstandsthermometer *n*

2397 RESISTANCE TO FLOW
f résistance *f* à l'écoulement
d Fliesswiderstand *m*

2398 RESISTIVITY
f résistivité *f*
d spezifischer Widerstand *m*

RESISTIVITY, apparent see 95
-, electrical see 632

2399 RESISTIVITY LOG
recording of electrical resistivity
versus depth
f diagraphie *f* de résistivité
d Widerstandslog *n*

2400 RESISTIVITY-SPACING CURVE
plot of apparent resistivity against
electrode spacing

f courbe *f* résistivité-espacement
d Widerstand-Elektrodenabstands-
kurve *f*

2401 RESISTIVITY SURVEY
complete study of a well or well
field by resistivity methods
f étude *f* des résistivités
d Widerstandsmessung *f*

2402 RESURGENT WATER
magmatic water of external origin
f eaux *f pl* résurgentes
d wiederkehrendes Grundwasser *n*

2403 RETENTION
detention of water on surface
depressions or in subsurface void
space; retention of water in pores
against gravity
f rétention *f*
d Haltungsvermögen *n*;
Rückhaltevermögen *n*

RETENTION, sieve see 2545
-, specific see 2619
-, surface see 2720

2404 RETURN FLOW
f reflux *m*
d Rückfluss *m*

2405 REVERSE CIRCULATION
method of circulating drilling fluid
downwards through the annulus and
upwards through the drill pipe
f circulation *f* inverse
d Gegenstromspülung *f*

2406 REVERSE FAULT
fault where relative movement of th
hanging wall has been in the upware
direction
f faille *f* inverse
d Wechsel *m*

2407 REVERSE ROTARY
rotary drilling with reverse circu
f forage *m* rotary inverse
d Rotaryverfahren *n* mit Gegen-
spülung

2408 RHYOLITE
very dense fine grained granitic r
f rhyolite *m*
d Rhyolith *m*

2409 RIDGE
elongated narrow elevation
f dorsale *m*; crête *f*
d Rücken *m*; Kamm *m*

2410 RIFT VALLEY
      surface depression due to the
      formation of graben block
      faulting
      f vallée *f* d'effondrement
      d Grabental *n*; Bruchtal *n*

2411 RINSE, TO
      f rincer
      d spülen

2412 RIPPEL MARK
      wavelike sculpture on water
      covered sand surfaces obtained
      by wave action
      f ride *f* de fond
      d Ripplemarke *f*

      RISE capillary see 242
      -, phreatic see 2218

2413 RISER
      pipe through which liquid rises in
      a well
      f colonne *f* montante
      d Steigrohr *n*

2414 RISER PIPE
      pipe through which water is raised
      in a production well
      f colonne *f* montante
      d Steigrohr *n*

2415 RISING SEGMENT
      part of hydrograph describing curve
      during precipitation
      f courbe *f* de concentration
      d steigender Kurvenast *m*

2416 RISING VELOCITY
      f vitesse *f* ascensionnelle
      d Steiggeschwindigkeit *f*

2417 RIVER
      natural water course through which
      runoff reaches sea
      f rivière *f*; fleuve *m*
      d Fluss *m*; Strom *m*

      RIVER, aggrading see 34
      -, consequent see 358
      -, obsequent see 2120
      -, resequent see 2389
      -, tidal see 2786

2418 RIVER BED
      channel of a river covered by its
      water
      f lit *m* d'une rivière
      d Flussbett *n*

2419 RIVER BEND
      f tournant *m* d'une fleuve
      d Flusschleife *f*

2420 RIVER BOTTOM
      f fond *m* de la rivière
      d Flussohle *f*

2421 RIVER REACH
      particular segment of a river
      f cours *m* d'un fleuve; bief *m*
      d Flusslauf *m*; Flussstrecke *f*

2422 RIVER SWAMP
      swamp in lowlands adjoining river
      f marécage *m* fluvial
      d Flussmorast *m*

2423 RIVER SYSTEM
      system of main river with all
      branches and tributaries
      f réseau *m* fluvial
      d Flusssystem *n*; Stromnetz *n*

2424 RIVER TERRACE
      level land terraces formed in a
      valley by fluviatile erosion or
      aggradation
      f terrasse *f* fluviale
      d Flussterrasse *f*

2425 RIVULET
      very small stream
      f ruisseau *m*
      d Rinnsal *n*

2426 ROCK
      consolidated mineral matter of
      igneous, sedimentary or chemical
      origin
      f roche *f*
      d Stein *m*; Gestein *n*

      ROCK, cavernous see 262
      -, clastic see 298
      -, consolidated see 359
      -, crystalline see 421
      -, detrital see 298
      -, extrusive see 698
      -, igneous see 998
      -, indurated see 1019
      -, intrusive see 1073
      -, unaltered see 2856

      ROCKS, carbonate see 248
      -, evaporite see 685

2427 ROCKFALL
      falling of bedrock from cliff or
      steep slope

f éboulement *m* de roches
d Steinfall *m*; Bergrutsch *m*

2428 ROCKFILL
f enrochement *m*
d Steinpackung *f*

2429 ROCK FORMATION
lithologically or structurally
distinct part of lithosphere
f formation *f*
d Gesteinsformation *f*

2430 ROCK SYSTEM
rocks deposited during a given
geologic time period
f système *m* lithologique
d Gesteinsfolge *f*

2431 ROCK TERRACE
terrace due to erosional action and
denudation
f terrasse *f* rocheuse
d Felsterrasse *f*

2432 ROCK TEXTURE
geometrical aspects and arrangement
of component particles of a rock
f texture *f* des roches
d Gesteinstextur *f*

2433 ROLLER BIT
drilling tool with a set of rotating
toothed rollers or cones
f outil *m* à molettes
d Rollenmeissel *m*

2434 ROOF DRAINAGE
precipitation runoff from roofs
f évacuation *f* des eaux de toiture
d Dachentwässerung *f*

2435 ROOT ZONE
zone in soil profile penetrated by
plant roots
f zone *f* radiculaire
d Wurzelzone *f*

2436 ROPE SOCKET
f cosse *f* de câble
d Kausche *f*; Kabelschuh *m*

ROTARY, hydraulic see 959
-, reverse see 2407

2437 ROTARY MOTION
f mouvement *m* de rotation
d Drehbewegung *f*

2438 ROTATING METER
stream velocity meter transforming

stream momentum into angular
momentum by vanes and rotor
f moulinet *m*
d Messflügel *m*

2439 ROTATING TABLE
horizontal round table that
transmits rotary movement to the
kelley and the drill pipe
f table *m* de rotation
d Drehtisch *m*

2440 ROUGHNESS
unevenness of surfaces giving rise
to high flow resistances
f rugosité *f*
d Rauhigkeit *f*

ROUGHNESS, bed see 170

2441 ROUGHNESS COEFFICIENT
coefficient describing roughness of
channel bed
f coefficient *m* de rugosité
d Rauhigkeitsbeiwert *m*;
   Bettrauhigkeitszahl *f*

2442 ROUNDNESS
degree to which a sand grain approa
spherical shape
f arrondi *m*
d Abrundung *f*

2443 ROUT, TO
action of predicting and directing
of flood waves through a channel
system
f propager
d weiterleiten

2444 RUNAROUND
working platform in rotary drilling
f passerelle *f* de derrick
d Arbeitsbühne *f*

2445 RUN DRY, TO
to cease to flow of a well or spring
f tarir
d versiegen

2446 RUNOFF
discharge of water through surface
streams of a drainage basin; sum o
surface runoff and ground water flo
that reaches the streams
f écoulement *m* de base; débit *m* d
   base; écoulement *m* total
d Abfluss *m*; Oberflächenabfluss *m*

RUNOFF, base see 149
-, direct (surface) see 514

2447   RUNOFF COEFFICIENT
       dimensionless coefficient to
       estimate runoff as a certain
       percentage of storm rainfall
       f   coefficient *m* de l'écoulement
           total
       d   Abflussbeiwert *m*

S

2448   SAFETY VALVE
    f   clapet *m* de sécurité
    d   Sicherheitsventil *n*

2449   SAFE YIELD
    amount of water withdrawn from
    basin without producing undesired
    result
    f   débit *m* de sécurité
    d   sichere Ausbeute *f*; sichere
       Entnahme *f*; sicheres Grund-
       wasserdargebot *n*

2450   SAFE YIELD OF STREAM
    lowest dry weather flow of a stream
    f   débit *m* de sécurité
    d   Sicherheitswert *m* der Entnahme

2451   SALINE SPRING
    spring water having high salt content
    f   source *f* chlorurée
    d   Solquelle *f*; Saline *f*

2452   SALINE WATER
    f   eau *f* salée
    d   Salzwasser *n*

2453   SALINITY LEVEL
    f   degré *m* de salinité
    d   Höhe *f* des Salzgehaltes

2454   SALINITY STRATIFICATION
    stratification of water in estuaries
    due to salinity-density difference
    f   stratification *f* par salinité
    d   Schichtung *f* nach dem Salz-
       gehalt

2455   SALTATION LOAD
    solid matter transported by stream
    by leaping movement over stream
    bed
    f   charge *f* en saltation
    d   Geröllfrachtung *f*; hüpfende
       Geschiebefrachtung *f*

2456   SALT DOME
    domelike intrusion of a mobile salt
    core into sedimentary rock
    f   dôme *m* de sel
    d   Salzdom *m*; Salzstock *m*

2457   SALT LAKE
    lake containing high salt concentra-
    tion usually with no outflow
    f   lac *m* salé
    d   Salzsee *m*

2458   SALT TOLERANCE
    resistance of crops to salt
    concentration
    f   résistance *f* à la salinité;
       résistance *f* au sel
    d   Salzfestigkeit *f*

2459   SALTY WATER
    water containing from 10,000 to
    100,000 ppm of total dissolved
    solids
    f   eau salée *f*
    d   Salzwasser *n*

    SAMPLE, disturbed see 531
    -, random see 2335
    -, soil see 2597
    -, water see 2953

    SAMPLER, snow see 2585

2460   SAMPLING
    taking of small quantities of water
    or porous media for further
    analysis
    f   prise *f* d'échantillon
    d   Probenahme *f*

2461   SAND
    unconsolidated detrital rock materia
    f   sable *m*
    d   Sand *m*

    SAND, clayey see 300
    -, clean see 305
    -, course see 3121
    -, drift see 566
    -, dune see 607
    -, fine see 728
    -, fine grained see 726
    -, medium see 2018
    -, shaly see 2525
    -, very fine see 2893

2462   SAND LINE;
    BOILING LINE
    cable operating the bailer
    f   câble *m* de curage
    d   Schöpfseil *n*

2463   SAND MODEL
    scaled down physical model of
    aquifer simulating boundary conditi

f modèle *m* en sable
d Sandkastenmodell *n*; Sandmodell *n*

SAND POINT, see drive point

2464 SAND PUMP
bailing device with a bottom valve
f cuiller *f*
d Sandpumpe *f*

2465 SAND SEPARATOR
device to remove sand granules
from well water
f séparateur *m* de sable
d Sandabscheider *m*

2466 SANDSTONE
f grés *m*
d Sandstein *m*

2467 SANITARY WELL PROTECTION
sealing of well to prevent entry of
pathogenic organisms
f protection *f* sanitaire d'un puits
d sanitärer Brunnenschutz *m*

2468 SAPROLITE
highly weakened metamorphic rock
f saprolite *m*
d Saprolith *m*

2469 SATURATED FLOW
(single phase) flow when all voids
are filled
f régime *m* d'écoulement saturé
d gesättigte Strömung *f*

SATURATION, gas see 820
-, irreducible see 1080
-, threshold see 2779

2470 SATURATION DEFICIENCY
f déficit *m* de saturation
d Sättigungsdefizit *n*

2471 SATURATION DISTRIBUTION
f distribution *f* de saturation
d Sättigungsverteilung *f*

2472 SATURATION POINT
f point *m* de saturation
d Sättigungspunkt *m*

2473 SATURATION PRESSURE
f pression *f* de saturation
d Sättigungsdruck *m*

2474 SATURATION REGIME
flow regime in completely
saturated porous medium

f régime *m* de saturation
d Sättigungsregime *n*

SATURATION VAPOR PRESSURE
see 2883

2475 SCALAR QUANTITY
f quantité *f* scalaire
d Skalare *f*; skalare Grösse *f*

2476 SCALE
very thin and flat rock fragment
f écaille *f*
d Schuppe *f*

2477 SCALE
accumulation of precipitated solid
material
f dépôt *m*
d Ansatz *m*

2478 SCALE
ratio of prototype to model
dimensions
f échelle *f*
d Masstab *m*

2479 SCALING FACTOR
ratio of characteristics of model to
those of prototype
f facteur *m* d'échelle
d Masstabbeiwert *m*

2480 SCHIST
foliated metamorphic rock
f schiste *m*
d Schiefer *m*

SCHIST, mica see 2040

2481 SCHISTOSITY
foliation of metamorphic rock
f schistosité *f*
d Schieferung *f*

2482 SCINTILLOMETER
f scintillomètre *m*
d Szintallationszähler *m*

2483 SCOUR
erosive action of running water in
streams
f affouillement *m*
d Tiefenschurf *m*

2484 SCREEN
f tamis *m*
d Sieb *n*

2485 SCREENING PLANT
f installation *f* de tamisage
d Siebanlage *f*

2486 SCREEN PIPE
slotted casing section positioned
opposite the producing horizon to
prevent inflow of sand into well
f crépine *f*
d Siebrohr *n*; Filterrohr *n*

2487 SEA LEVEL
averaged height of the surface of
the sea used as datum for elevations
f niveau *m* de la mer
d Meeresspiegel *m*; Seehöhe *f*

2488 SEALING-GROUT
cement grout injected between casing
and bore hole wall to seal off aquifer
from external contamination
f laitier *m* de ciment
d Abdichtungszementbrühe *f*

2489 SEAMLESS PIPE
f tube *m* sans soudure
d nahtloses Rohr *n*

2490 SEASONAL VARIATION
f variation *f* saisonnière
d jahreszeitliche Schwankung *f*

2491 SEA WATER INTRUSION
encroachment of sea water into a
coastal aquifer
f invasion *m* des eaux salées
d Eindringen *n* von Meerwasser

2492 SECONDARY INTERSTICES
voids formed after rocks had
been formed
f interstices *mpl* secondaires
d sekundäre Hohlräume *mpl*

2493 SECONDARY POROSITY
porosity created after deposition
of sediment due to fracturing,
leaching etc.
f porosité *f* secondaire
d sekundäre Porosität *f*

2494 SEDIMENTARY DEPOSIT
f dépôt *m* sédimentaire
d Sedimentablagerung *f*

2495 SEDIMENTATION
deposition of solid disintegrated
rock material by water, wind or
gravity transport
f sédimentation *f*
d Sedimentation *f*

2496 SEDIMENT TRANSPORT
all transport of eroded rock material
by moving water or wind
f transports *mpl* solides;
transport *m* de sédiments
d Sedimenttransport *m*;
Sedimentfrachtung *f*

2497 SEEPAGE
slow flow through a filter, small
opening or porous medium; movement
of water in unsaturated soil
f suintement *m*; écoulement *m* par
infiltration
d Sickerung *f*; Sickerströmung *f*

SEEPAGE, storm see 2690
-, surface see 2722

2498 SEEPAGE COEFFICIENT
f coefficient *m* d'infiltration
d Filterkoeffizient *m*

SEEPAGE LOSS, canal see 233

2499 SEEPAGE PATH
trajectory of fluid particles in
seepage flow
f chemin *m* d'infiltration
d Sickerweg *m*

2500 SEEPAGE RATE
velocity of seepage flow
f vitesse *f* d'infiltration
d Sickerrate *f*; Sickergeschwindig-
keit *f*

2501 SEEPAGE SPRING;
FILTRATION SPRING
spring where surface discharge
occurs from numerous small openin
f source *f* de ruissellement;
source *f* d'infiltration
d Sickerquelle *f*; flächenhafter
Grundwasseraustritt *m*

2502 SEEPAGE SURFACE
outflow surface between water level
and intersection of the phreatic sur
with well
f surface *f* de suintement
d Sickerfläche *f*; Sickerstrecke *f*

SEEPAGE VELOCITY
see Darcy velocity

SEGMENT, approach see 96
-, crest see 405
-, recession see 2356
-, rising see 2415

2503 SEISMIC PROFILE
    f profil *m* sismique; coupe *f*
       sismique
    d seismisches Profil *n*

2504 SEISMIC REFLECTION
    reflection of a seismic ray on a
    lithologic interface
    f réflexion *f* sismique
    d seismische Reflextion *f*

2505 SEISMIC REFRACTION
    refraction of a seismic wave at a
    lithologic interface
    f réfraction *f* sismique
    d seismische Refraktion *f*;
       seismische Brechung *f*

2506 SEISMIC WAVE
    wave generated by a seismic
    impulse or explosion
    f onde *f* sismique
    d seismische Welle *f*;
       Erschütterungswelle *f*

2507 SEISMOMETER
    detector of seismic waves
    f sismomètre *m*
    d Seismometer *n*

2508 SELECTIVE ABSORPTION
    f absorption *f* sélective
    d Selektivabsorption *f*;
       selektive Absorption *f*

2509 SELF-CLEANING CAPACITY
    capacity of a river to clean its
    water from pollutants over a given
    length of water course
    f pouvoir *m* auto-épurateur
    d Selbstreinigungskraft *f*

2510 SELF-POTENTIAL
    natural electric potential occurring
    in a well
    f potentiel *m* spontané
    d Eigenpotential *n*

2511 SENSIBLE HEAT
    f chaleur *f* sensible
    d wahrnehmbare Wärme *f*

2512 SEPARATION
    f séparation *f*
    d Loslösung *f*; Trennung *f*

    SEPARATION, hydrograph see 970
    -, sand see 2465
    -, water see 2954

2513 SERIES
    subdivision of rock according to
    age at which they were laid down
    in a geologic epoch
    f série *f* lithologique
    d Schichtenfolge *f*

2514 SERPENTINE
    metamorphic product of peridotites
    f serpentine *f*
    d Serpentin *m*

2515 SETTING OF CEMENT
    process of hardening of cement
    f prise *f* du ciment
    d Abbinden *n* des Zements

2516 SETTLING BASIN
    basin used for settling out of solids
    from suspensions
    f bassin *m* de décantation
    d Absetzbecken *n*

2517 SETTLING PIT
    f bac *m* de décantation
    d Klärbecken *n*

2518 SETTLING VELOCITY
    terminal velocity at which a
    particle will fall through a fluid
    f vitesse *f* limite de sédimentation;
       vitesse *f* de décantation
    d Absetzgeschwindigkeit *f*

2519 SEWAGE
    domestic and municipal wastes
    f eaux *f pl* d'égouts
    d Abwasser *n*

2520 SEWAGE TREATMENT
    f traitement *m* des eaux d'égouts;
       épuration *f* des eaux d'égouts
    d Abwasserreinigung *f*;
       Abwasserbehandlung *f*

2521 SHAFT
    vertical and usually large diameter
    hole penetrating geologic formations
    for access of subsurface points
    f puits *m*
    d Schacht *m*

2522 SHAFT
    axis transmitting or receiving
    rotational movement
    f arbre *m*
    d Welle *f*

    SHALE, bentonitic see 174

2523 SHALE LINE
line connecting points of zero
potential in a self potential log
f ligne *f* de base des marnes
d Basislinie *f*

2524 SHALLOW WELL
f puits *m* peu profond
d Flachbrunnen *m*

2525 SHALY SAND
sand containing considerable
amounts of clay and shales
f sable *m* argileux
d toniger Sand *m*

SHAPE, basin see 161
-, grain see 863
-, spherical see 2624

2526 SHATTERED FAULT ZONE
f zone *f* de broyage; zone *f*
fracturée d'un système de failles
d Rüschelzone *f*

2527 SHEAR
f cisaillement *m*
d Scherung *f*

2528 SHEAR INTENSITY
f intensité *f* de cisaillement
d Scherintensität *f*

2529 SHEAR STRENGTH
f résistance *f* au cisaillement
d Scherfestigkeit *f*

2530 SHEAR VELOCITY
f vitesse *f* de cisaillement
d Schergeschwindigkeit *f*

2531 SHEAR WAVE
f onde *f* transversale
d Transversalwelle *f*; Scherwelle *f*

2532 SHEAVE
f poulie *f*
d Scheibe *f*

2533 SHEET EROSION
erosion occurring over widespread
tabular sedimentary or effusive rock
f érosion *f* en nappe
d Flächenerosion *f*

2534 SHEET FLOW
shallow flow of extrusive lava over
wide area
f épanchement *m* effusif en couche
d Flächenerguss *m*; Arealeruption *f*

2535 SHIELD
geologically stable and undisturbed
continental block
f bouclier *m*
d Schild *m*

2536 SHOCK POINT
point at which seismic impulse is
applied to system under study
f point *m* de choc
d Schockpunkt *m*

2537 SHOCK WAVE
f onde *f* de choc
d Stosswelle *f*

SHOE, casing see 256
-, guide see 912

2538 SHORE
zone of separation between land and
moving water
f rivage *m*
d Ufer *n*

2539 SHOT DRILLING
method of drilling where shot droppe
into the bore hole through the drill
pipe exercises abrasive action on the
bottom hole
f sondage *m* à la grenaille
d Schrotbohren *n*

2540 SHOT POINT
point where explosive charge is set
off in seismic survey
f point *m* de tir
d Schusspunkt *m*

2541 SIDE WALL
wall of a well
f paroi *f* d'un puits
d Brunnenwandung *f*

2542 SIEVE
f tamis *m*
d Sieb *n*

2543 SIEVE ANALYSIS
mechanical grain size analysis by
sieving
f granulométrie *f* mécanique
d Siebanalyse *f*

2544 SIEVE OPENING
opening between mesh wires of a
sieve
f ouverture *f* de maille
d lichte Maschenweite *f*

2545 SIEVE RETENTION
      material retained on a sieve
      f retenue *f* au tamis
      d Siebrückstand *m*

      SILICA, see silicon dioxide

      SILICA, amorphous see 66

2546 SILICATE ROCK
      rock containing silica in predomi-
      nant proportions
      f roches *fpl* siliceuses
      d Silikatgestein *n*

2547 SILICIC ACID
      H_4SiO_4 monomeric
      f acide *m* silicique
      d Kieselsäure *f*

2548 SILICON BRASS
      f laiton *m* siliceux
      d Siliziummessing *m*

2549 SILICON BRONZE
      f bronze *m* siliceux
      d Siliziumbronze *f*

2550 SILICON DIOXIDE
      silica, SiO_2
      f silice *f*; oxyde *m* de silicium
      d Siliziumdioxyd *n*; Kieselerde *f*;
         Silikat *n*

2551 SILL
      concordant magma intrusion between
      sedimentary beds
      f filon-couche *m*
      d Lagergang *m*

2552 SILL
      submarine separation of different
      basins
      f seuil *m*
      d Schwelle *f*

2553 SILT
      particle diameter 0.05 to 0.005 mm
      (USBS)
      f silt *m*
      d Schluff *m*

2554 SILTING
      deposition of silt, especially in
      reservoirs
      f envasement *m*
      d Anschwemmung *f*; Verschlickung *f*

2555 SILTSTONE
      f phtanite *m*
      d Tongestein *n*

2556 SILURIAN
      geologic period of the Paleozoic era
      f Silurien *m*
      d Silur *n*

2557 SILVER IODIDE
      AgI, chemical substance used as
      condensation nuclei in weather
      modification experiments
      f iodure *m* d'argent
      d Silberjodit *m*

      SIMILARITY, dynamic see 611
      -, geometric see 835
      -, kinematic see 1111

2558 SIMILARITY CRITERIA
      conditions indicating under what
      circumstances a model and prototype
      are similar
      f conditions *fpl* de similitude
      d Ähnlichkeitsbedingungen *fpl*

2559 SIMPLE HYDROGRAPH
      single peaked hydrograph
      f hydrogramme *m* simple
      d einfache Abflussganglinie *f*

2560 SINGLE OUTLET
      stream cutting through divide
      (tributary basin); outflow into sea
      (major basin)
      f exutoire *m* unique
      d Auslass *m*

2561 SINK
      (mathematical)
      f puits *m*
      d Senke *f*

2562 SINKER BAR
      heavy bar rod above bit in cable
      drilling
      f tige *f* de battage
      d Schwerstange *f*

2563 SINK HOLE
      hole in karstic limestone terrane
      through which water escapes
      underground
      f doline *f*
      d Doline *f*; Karsttrichter *m*

2564 SIPHON
      f siphon *m*
      d Siphon *m*; Saugheber *m*

2565 SIPHONING
      f siphonnage *m*
      d Saughebewirkung *f*

SIZE, grain see 864
-, mesh see 2030

2566 SKIN EFFECT
effect of the zone of reduced
permeability immediately around
the borehole on transient flow
phenomena (in pumping tests)
f effet *m* pariétal
d Hauteffekt *m*

2567 SLAG
congealed lava, scoria
f scorie *f*
d Schlacke *f*; vulkanische
Schlacke *f*

2568 SLATE
metamorphic rock showing well
developed cleavage
f ardoise *f*
d Schiefer *m*; Plattenschiefer *m*

2569 SLEDGE
heavy hammer
f maillet *m*; masse *f*
d Fäustel *m*

2570 SLICKENSIDE
polished fault plane with grooves
due to relative motion of fault
blocks
f miroir *m* de faille
d Rutschspiegel *m*

2571 SLIDING
downslope movement of rock and
earth material
f glissement *m*
d Abgleiten *n*

2572 SLIPS
wedges to hold drill pipe while
adding a new length of pipe in
rotary drilling
f coins *mpl* de retenue
d Fangkeile *mpl*

2573 SLOPE
inclination of a surface
f pente *f*
d Gefälle *n*; Hang *m*

SLOPE, continental see 371
-, ground see 890
-, water surface see 2961

2574 SLOTTED PIPE
f crépine *f* à fentes
d Siebrohr *n*

2575 SLOTTED PLATE
f tôle *f* perforée
d Siebblech *n*

2576 SLUSH BUCKET
bucket shaped bailer
f cuiller *f*
d Sandpumpe *f*; Schmandlöffel *m*

2577 SLUSH PIT
settling pit for drilling mud
f bac *m* de décantation
d Absetzbecken *n*

2578 SNOW
solid crystalline form of water
f neige *f*
d Schnee *m*

2579 SNOW COVER;
SNOWPACK
accumulated height of snow covering
a given area
f couche *f* de neige
d Schneedecke *f*

2580 SNOW DENSITY
f densité *f* de la neige
d Schneedichte *f*

2581 SNOWDRIFT
snow accumulation due to wind
transport
f congère *f*
d Schneewehe *f*

2582 SNOW GAGE
f nivomètre *m*
d Schneeniederschlagsmesser *m*

2583 SNOW LINE
line connecting elevations above
which snowpack remains throughout
the year
f limite *f* des neiges éternelles
d Schneegrenze *f*

2584 SNOW MELT
f fonte *f* de neige
d Schneeschmelze *f*

SNOWPACK, see snow cover

2585 SNOW SAMPLER
tube taking cylindrical samples
through the snow profile
f échantillonneur *m* de neige
d Schneeprobenehmer *m*;
Schneeausstecher *m*

2586 SNOW STAKE
 f échelle _f_ de neige
 d Schneepegel _m_

 SOCKET, bell see 171
 -, rope see 2436

2587 SOD
 root system in the soil
 f système _m_ de racines
 d Wurzelwerk _n_

2588 SODIUM
 Na
 f sodium _m_
 d Natrium _n_

 SOIL, azonal see 126
 -, halomorphic see 918
 -, lateritic see 1137

2589 SOIL AGGREGATE
 loosely cemented cluster of soil
 particles
 f agrégat _m_ des particules de sol
 d Bodenaggregat _n_

2590 SOILCOVER
 layer of soil material covering the
 bedrock
 f couverture _f_ de sol
 d Bodendecke _f_; Bodenkrume _f_

2591 SOIL MECHANICS
 science dealing with the mechanical
 properties of soils
 f mécanique _f_ des sols
 d Bodenmechanik _f_

2592 SOIL-MOISTURE METER
 device to record soil moisture in situ
 f appareil _m_ de mesure de l'humidité
    du sol
 d Bodenfeuchtemessgerät _n_

2593 SOIL-MOISTURE SUCTION
 negative pore pressure exerted by
 capillary forces
 f succion _f_ de l'eau dans le sol
 d Saugwirkung _f_ des Bodenwassers

2594 SOIL MOISTURE TENSION
 negative pore pressure
 f tension _f_ de l'eau dans le sol
 d Bodenfeuchtesaugspannung _f_

2595 SOIL PARTICLE
 f particule _f_ de sol
 d Bodenpartikel _n_; Bodenteilchen

2596 SOIL PROFILE
 vertical section of soil mantle
 usually with distinguishable soil
 horizons (A,B,C)
 f section _f_ du sol
 d Bodenprofil _n_

 SOIL PROFILE, zonal see 3032

2597 SOIL SAMPLE
 sample of soil on which soil
 properties are to be determined
 f échantillon _m_ de sol
 d Bodenprobe _f_

2598 SOIL STRUCTURE
 f structure _f_ du sol
 d Bodenstruktur _f_

2599 SOIL SURFACE
 f surface _f_ du sol
 d Bodenoberfläche _f_

2600 SOIL SWELLING
 volume increase of soil due to
 swelling of unsaturated clay
 particles when in contact with water
 f gonflement _m_ du sol
 d Bodenquellung _f_

2601 SOIL WATER
 gravity and pellicular water
 contained in the soil zone
 f eau _f_ du sol
 d Bodenfeuchte _f_; Bodenwasser _n_

2602 SOILWATER ZONE
 upper portion of the zone of aeration
 containing soil water; belt of soil
 water
 f zone _f_ d'évaporation; zone _f_
    au voisinage du sol
 d bodennahe Zone _f_; Bodenwasser-
    gürtel _m_

2603 SOLAR RADIATION
 f irradiation _f_ solaire
 d Sonnenstrahlung _f_

2604 SOLID MATRIX
 assembly of interconnected solid
 mineral grains surrounded by voids
 f phase _f_ solide
 d Festkörpergerüst _n_

2605 SOLID VOLUME
 volume of the solid particles in a
 porous sample
 f volume _m_ de la phase solide;
    volume _m_ des pleins
 d Festkörpervolumen _n_

2606 SOLIFLUCTION
slow flowage of mud streams in
arctic regions
f solifluction *f*
d Solifluktion *f*

2607 SOLUBILITY
f solubilité *f*
d Löslichkeit *f*

2608 SOLUM
top layers of soil profile
f sol *m* arrable
d Ackerkrume *f*

SOLUTION, analog see 71
-, buffered see 208
-, numerical see 2118

SONDE, monoelectrode see 2072

2609 SONDE SPACING
distance between measuring and
current electrodes
f espacement *m* de la sonde
d Messlänge *f* einer Anordnung

2610 SONIC GENERATOR
f générateur *m* de son
d Schallerzeuger *m*

2611 SOUND VELOCITY
f vitesse *f* du son
d Schallgeschwindigkeit *f*

2612 SOURCE
(mathematical)
f source *f*
d Quellpunkt *m*

SOURCE, neutron see 2109

2613 SOURCE CHAMBER
f chambre *f* de captage
d Quellstube *f*

SPACE, pore see 2269
-, total pore see 2808
-, vugular pore see 2910

SPACING, electrode see 636
-, sonde see 2609
-, well see 3001

2614 SPECIFIC CAPACITY
ratio of well discharge to
corresponding drawdown
f débit *m* spécifique
d Brunnenergiebigkeitsmass *n*;
spezifische Ergiebigkeit *f*

2615 SPECIFIC DENSITY
f densité *f*
d Dichte *f*

SPECIFIC DISCHARGE
see Darcy velocity

2616 SPECIFIC DRAWDOWN
amount of drawdown per unit
discharge in a well
f rabattement *m* spécifique
d spezifische Absenkung *f*

2617 SPECIFIC ELECTRICAL
CONDUCTANCE
conductance of a cube of solution
(1 cm^3)
f conductivité
d spezifische Leitfähigkeit *f*

2618 SPECIFIC GRAVITY
f poids *m* spécifique
d spezifisches Gewicht *n*

2619 SPECIFIC RETENTION;
WATER RETAINING CAPACITY
water held against gravity forces
f eau *f* de rétention; capacité *f*
de rétention; pouvoir *m* de
rétention d'eau
d spezifisches Wasserhaltungsver-
mögen *n*; Wasserrückhalte-
vermögen *n*

2620 SPECIFIC SURFACE
ratio of grain particle surface to
volume of grain particles
f surface *f* spécifique
d spezifische Oberfläche *f*

2621 SPECIFIC VOLUME
f volume *m* spécifique
d spezifisches Volumen *n*

2622 SPECIFIC YIELD
water drained from soil under
gravity flow
f débit *m* spécifique; eau *f* de
gravité; capacité *f* de libre
écoulement
d spezifische Ergiebigkeit *f*

2623 SPELEOLOGY
exploration and study of undergrour
caverns
f spéléologie *f*
d Höhlenkunde *f*

2624 SPHERICAL SHAPE
f forme *f* sphérique
d kugelförmige Gestalt *f*

2625 SPILLWAY
      device for the escape of excess
      water
      f déversoir *m*
      d Überfallwehr *n*; Wehr *n*

2626 SPONTANEOUS POTENTIAL
      natural electrical potential
      measured in well; self-potential
      f potentiel *m* spontané
      d Eigenpotential *n*

2627 SPRING
      localized natural hydraulic discharge
      of water at surface resulting in a
      small rivulet
      f source *f*
      d Quelle *f*

      SPRING, artesian see 114
      -, barrier see 144
      -, boundary see 197
      -, carbonated see 247
      -, channel see 280
      -, contact see 368
      -, cool see 385
      -, depression see 468
      -, dimple see 507
      -, filtration see 2501
      -, fracture see 783
      -, gravity see 885
      -, intermittant see 1062
      -, medicinal see 2017
      -, mineral see 2048
      -, perennial see 2195
      -, saline see 2451
      -, seepage see 2501
      -, subaqueous see 2681
      -, thermal see 2769
      -, tubular see 2849
      -, unconformity see 2861
      -, valley see 2880
      -, warm see 2914

2628 SPRING, TO
      action of water originating or
      rising from a spring
      f jaillir
      d entspringen; hervorquellen

2629 SPUDDER
      f installation *f* de forage pour
         l'avant-trou
      d Vorbohrer *m*

2630 STAFF GAGE
      fixed graduated scale
      f échelle *f* limnimétrique
      d Messlatte *f*; Lattenpegel *m*

2631 STAGE
      water surface elevation at a point
      (along stream, in lake, etc.) above
      an arbitrary datum
      f hauteur *f* d'eau
      d Wasserstand *m*; Höhe *f* des
         Wasserspiegels

      STAGE, water see 2958

2632 STAGE-DISCHARGE RELATION
      see rating curve
      f courbe *f* de tarage
      d Bezugskurve *f*; Abflusskurve *f*

2633 STAGE HYDROGRAPH
      elevation of stage plotted against
      time
      f relation *f* hauteur - temps
      d Wasserstandsganglinie *f*

2634 STAGE INDICATOR
      f indicateur *m* limnimétrique
      d Standanzeiger *m*; Wasserstands-
         anzeiger *m*

2635 STAGE RECORD
      stage discharge relations presented
      in tabulated form
      f tableau *m* des hauteurs
      d Abflusstafel *f*

2636 STAGNATION POINT
      foremost point on streamline
      dividing area of pumping depression
      from zone of influence in a tilted
      aquifer being pumped by one well
      f point *m* de stagnation
      d untere Scheitelung *f*;
         Kulminationspunkt *m*

2637 STAINLESS STEEL
      f acier *m* inoxydable
      d rostfreier Stahl *m*

2638 STALACTITE
      dripstone hanging from cavern roof
      f stalactite *m*
      d Stalaktit *m*

2639 STALAGMITE
      dripstone column rising from cavern
      floor
      f stalagmite *m*
      d Stalagmit *m*

      STANDARD COEFFICIENT OF
      PERMEABILITY
      see laboratory coefficient

2640 STANDARD DEVIATION
measure of variability of square
of individual deviations from
their mean
f écart-type *m*
d Standardabweichung *f*

2641 STANDARD TOOL
percussion, cable tool in cable
drilling
f installation *f* de forage
   standard
d Standardbohrgerät *n*

2642 STATE OF SOLUTION
degree to which a mineral or rock
has gone into solution
f degré *m* de dissolution
d Lösungszustand *m*

STATION, gaging see 808
-, hydrometric see 980
-, pumping see 2307

2643 STATISTICAL ANALYSIS
f analyse *f* statistique
d statistische Analyse *f*

2644 STEADY FLOW
flow where velocity at a point
remains constant with respect to
time
f écoulement *m* permanent
d stetige Strömung *f*

2645 STEEP
property of inclination with very
great gradient
f à pente raide; abrupt
d steil

2646 STEMFLOW
rain water flowing down stem
of plants
f ruissellement *m* le long du tronc
d Stammabfluss *m*

2647 STEREOGRAM
block diagram, three dimensional
diagram
f diagramme *m* stéréoscopique
d Blockbild *n*

2648 STILLING WELL
well connected to a flowing stream
through a bottom conduit permitting
elevation measures to be taken in
quiescent water
f puits *m* de mesure
d Beruhigungsschacht *m*

2649 STOMATAL TRANSPIRATION
transpiration by escape of water
through pores (stomata) of leaves
f transpiration *f* par stomata
d stomatäre Transpiration *f*

STORAGE, aquifer see 101
-, bank see 138
-, pocket see 2253
-, prism see 2296
-, wedge see 2976

2650 STORAGE CAPACITY
a) ability of an aquifer to store
   water;
b) capacity of rivers to store water
   in their own channel
f capacité *f* d'emmagasinement
d Speicherfähigkeit *f*; Wasser-
   aufnahmefähigkeit *f*; Speicher-
   vermögen *n*; Rückhaltevermögen

2651 STORAGE COEFFICIENT
volume of water stored or released
from a column of aquifer with unit
cross section under unit pressure
decline
f coefficient *m* d'emmagasinement;
   storativité *f*; coefficient *m* de
   stockage
d Speicherkoeffizient *m*;
   Speicherungsbeiwert *m*

2652 STORAGE GAGE
precipitation gage collecting and
storing total amount of inflowing
water to be read at long intervals
f pluviomètre *m* totalisateur
d Niederschlagssammler *m*;
   Totalisator *m*

2653 STORAGE IN DEPRESSIONS
water retention in surface depressi
f stockage *m* dans les dépression
   du sol
d Wasserspeicherung *f* in Senken

2654 STORM
a) disturbance of average meteoro
   logical conditions usually conne
   with precipitation
b) period of precipitation over a
   specific drainage basin
f averse *f*; grain *m*; orage *m*; te
d Niederschlagsfall *m*, Regenfall
   Schauer *m*; Gewitter *n*; Sturm *m*

STORM, design see 481

2655 STORM INTENSITY PATTERN
   f hyétogramme *m*
   d Verteilung *f* der Niederschlags-
      intensität

STORM RUNOFF, see direct
runoff

STORM SEEPAGE, see subsurface
runoff

2656 STOVE PIPE
   double wall casing, as introduced
   by California stove pipe drilling
   method
   f tubage *m* double
   d Doppelverrohrung *f*

STRAINER, micro see 2043
-, suction see 2699

2657 STRATH TERRACE
   erosional remnant of elevated
   broad river valley
   f terrasse *f* du replat de versant
   d Erosionsterrasse *f* im
      Vorrumpf

2658 STRATIFICATION
   depositional structure of sedimentary rocks in beds and layers
   f stratification *f*
   d Schichtung *f*

STRATIFICATION, salinity see
2454
-, thermal see 2770

2659 STRATIGRAPHY
   study of stratified rock
   f stratigraphie *f*
   d Stratigraphie *f*

2660 STRATUM
   sedimentary bed or layer
   f couche *f*; lit *m*
   d Schicht *f*

STRATUM, confining see 350

2661 STRAY CURRENTS
   random electrical currents
   originating from leaks in electrical
   circuits
   f courants *mpl* vagabonds
   d Streuströme *fpl*

2662 STREAM
   a body of flowing water
   f fleuve *m*; rivière *f*
   d Strom *m*; Fluss *m*

STREAM, adjusted see 26
-, antecedent see 90
-, continuous see 372
-, effluent see 628
-, ephemeral see 659
-, gaining see 628
-, influent see 1032
-, insulated see 1045
-, intermittent see 1063
-, interrupted see 1066
-, losing see 1032
-, natural see 2102
-, subterranean see 2692

STREAMS, perennial see 2196

2663 STREAM BED
   bottom of stream covered by water
   f lit *m* d'une rivière
   d Flussbett *n*

2664 STREAM CHANNEL
   f chenal *m*
   d Rinne *f*; Flusslauf *m*

2665 STREAM DEVELOPMENT
   ratio of actual tortuous stream
   length between two points on straight
   line connecting these points
   f développement *m* du cours
   d Stromentwicklung *f*

2666 STREAM FLOW
   total runoff confined in stream and
   channels
   f écoulement *m* total
   d Gesamtabfluss *m*

2667 STREAM FREQUENCY
   channel frequency, number of stream
   segments per unit area
   f fréquence *f* des éléments du réseau
   d Flussstreckenhäufigkeit *f*

2668 STREAMING POTENTIAL
   electrical potential difference
   created by flow through a porous
   medium
   f potentiel *m* électrocinétique
   d Strömungspotential *n*

2669 STREAMLINE
   line to which flow velocity vectors
   are tangent
   f ligne *f* de courant
   d Stromlinie *f*

2670 STREAM ORDER
hierarchic order of stream segments
according to tributaires
f numéro *m* d'ordre d'un cours
d'eau
d Ordnungsstufe *f* eines Flusses

2671 STREAM PROFILE
elevation of main stream bed as a
function of distance from outflow
f profil *m* en long d'une rivière
d Flussprofil *n*; hydrologischer
Längsschnitt *m*

2672 STREAMTUBE
imaginary tube of fluid bounded by
streamlines
f filet *m* fluide
d Stromfaden *m*

STRENGTH, breaking see 200
-, compressive see 335
-, sheer see 2529
-, tensile see 2757

STRESS, intergranular see 1061

2673 STRESS LIMIT
f tension *f* limite
d Grenzbelastung *f*

2674 STRIKE
direction of the line of intersection
of a bed or other structural
feature with the horizontal
f direction *f*
d Streichen *n*

2675 STRIKE VALLEY
valley following strike of underlying strata
f vallée *f* subséquente
d Nachfolgetal *n*; subsequentes
Tal *n*

2676 STRINGER
irregular vein cutting through a
rock mass
f filet *m* irrégulier
d unregelmässiger Gang *m*;
Erzschnur *f*

2677 STRUCTURAL DOME
f dôme *m* de structure
d Strukturdom *m*

2678 STRUCTURAL FACTOR
features modifying or interrupting
continuity of rock types
f facteur *m* de structure
d Strukturfaktor *m*

2679 STRUCTURAL GEOLOGY
part of geology dealing with the
structures of rock
f géologie *f* structurale;
tectonique *f*
d Strukturgeologie *f*; tektonische
Geologie *f*

STRUCTURE, chaotic see 281
-, massive see 1194
-, soil see 2598

2680 STUFFING BOX
f presse - étoupe *m*
d Stopfbüchse *f*

2681 SUBAQUEOUS SPRING
springs discharging below surfaces
of water bodies such as oceans,
lakes and rivers
f exutoire *m* subaquatique
d subaquatische Quelle *f*;
Grundquelle *f*

2682 SUBARTESIAN WELL
artesian well (cf.) with insufficient
head to raise water above land
surface
f puits *m* artésien sans écoulement
libre
d subartesischer Brunnen *m*

2683 SUBLIMATION
direct conversion of water from its
solid state to the vapor phase
f sublimation *f*
d Sublimation *f*

2684 SUBMERSIBLE PUMP
f pompe *f* immergée; pompe *f*
submersible
d Tauchpumpe *f*; Unterwasser-
pumpe *f*

2685 SUBPERMAFROST WATER
groundwater below the permafrost
f eau *f* sous la zone de pergelisol
d Grundwasser *n* unter der Gefror

2686 SUBSEQUENT RIVER
river flowing along strike of a weak
formation; tributary of a consequen
river
f rivière *f* subséquente
d Nachfolgefluss *m*; subsequenter
Fluss *m*

2687 SUBSIDING WATER
f eau *f* en décrue
d fallendes Wasser *n*

2688 SUBSOIL
      f sous-sol *m*
      d Untergrund *m*

2689 SUBSURFACE FLOW
      see subsurface runoff
      f écoulement *m* souterrain
      d unterirdischer Abfluss *m*

2690 SUBSURFACE RUNOFF;
      STORM SEEPAGE; SUBSURFACE
      FLOW; SUBSURFACE STORM
      FLOW
      runoff due to infiltrated precipitation
      moving laterally under surface
      f écoulement *m* hypodermique
      d unechter Grundwasserabfluss *m*

2691 SUBTERRANEAN
      beneath the surface of the earth
      f souterrain
      d unterirdisch

2692 SUBTERRANEAN STREAM
      stream flowing through very large
      caves and caverns underground
      f fleuve *m* souterrain
      d unterirdischer Fluss *m*

2693 SUCCESSION OF FORMATIONS
      f succession *f* stratigraphique;
         suite *f* de couches
      d Schichtenfolge *f*

      SUCTION, soil-moisture see 2593

2694 SUCTION HEAD
      f hauteur *f* d'aspiration
      d Saughöhe *f*

2695 SUCTION LIFT
      height to which a pump can aspire
      a liquid
      f hauteur *f* d'aspiration
      d Saughöhe *f*

2696 SUCTION LIMIT
      f limite *f* de succion
      d Grenzsaugfähigkeit *f*

2697 SUCTION LINE
      tubular connection line through
      which liquid is aspired into pump
      f tuyeau *m* d'aspiration
      d Saugleitung *f*

2698 SUCTION PUMP
      f pompe *f* aspirante
      d Saugpumpe *f*

2699 SUCTION STRAINER
      f crépine *f* filtrante
      d Filterkorb *m*

2700 SULFATE
      SO_4
      f sulfate *m*
      d Sulfat *n*

2701 SULFURIC ACID
      H_2SO_4
      f acide *m* sulfurique
      d Schwefelsäure *f*

2702 SUMMATION CURVE
      curve of cumulated values
      f courbe *f* cumulative
      d Summenkurve *f*

2703 SUMMIT
      highest point of a physiographic
      feature
      f sommet *m*
      d Gipfel *m*

2704 SUMP
      pumping pit from where pump lifts
      water by suction
      f puisard *m*
      d Pumpensumpf *m*; Sumpf *m*

2705 SUNKEN PAN
      evaporation pan buried in the ground
      for equal elevation of water surface
      and ground surface
      f bac *m* enterré
      d versenkter Landverdunstungskessel *m*

2706 SUPERIMPOSED VALLEY
      valley established on surface in
      pattern independent of underlying
      rock structure
      f vallée *f* surimposée; percée *f*
         épigénétique
      d aufgesetztes Tal *n*; epigenetisches
         Tal *n*

2707 SUPERPOSITION
      f superposition *f*
      d Superposition *f*

2708 SUPERSATURATION
      f supersaturation *f*; saturation *f*
         excédentaire; sursaturation *f*
      d Übersättigung *f*

      SUPPLY, surface water see 2726
      -, water see 2960

2709 SUPPLY SYSTEM
f réseau *m* d'alimentation
d Versorgungsnetz *n*

2710 SUPRAPERMAFROST WATER
ground water above permafrost
f eau *f* au dessus de la zone de
pergelisol
d Grundwasser *n* über der Gefrornis

2711 SURF
f déferlement *m*
d Brandung *f*

SURFACE, erosion see 670
-, land see 1127
-, phreatic see 2219
-, piezometric see 2232
-, receiving see 2350
-, seepage see 2502
-, soil see 2599
-, specific see 2620

2712 SURFACE AREA REDUCTION
f réduction *f* de la superficie
d Oberflächenverkleinerung *f*

2713 SURFACE CASING
part of well casing extending above
land surface; standpipe
f colonne *f* de surface
d Standrohr *n*

2714 SURFACE DETENTION
sheet flow of water in overland
flow before channel is reached
f stockage *m* de surface;
rétention *f* provisoire
d Oberflächenrückhaltung *f*;
Oberflächenspeicherung *f*

2715 SURFACE ENTRY
opening immediately at land
surface permitting infiltration to
take place
f entrée *m* de surface
d Eindringöffnung *f*

2716 SURFACE EQUIPMENT
f appareillage *m* de surface
d Übertageausrüstung *f*

2717 SURFACE FILM
(monomolecular) film of organic
compounds forming on water or
grain surface
f film *m* de surface; pellicule *f*
de surface
d Oberflächenfilm *m*

2718 SURFACE MAPPING
topographic and geodetic mapping
of an area (as opposed to geologic
mapping)
f levée *f* topographique
d topographische Kartierung *f*

2719 SURFACE MINE
strip mine
f exploitation *f* minière à ciel
ouvert
d Tagebau *m*

2720 SURFACE RETENTION
water held on land surface
f rétention *f* dans les dépressions
du sol
d Oberflächenrückhaltung *f*;
Wasserspeicherung *f* an der
Bodenoberfläche

2721 SURFACE RUNOFF
part of runoff travelling over ground
surface and through channels
f ruissellement *m* de surface
d Oberflächenabfluss *m*

2722 SURFACE SEEPAGE
surface discharge of ground water
not important enough to form
rivulet
f suintement *m* de surface
d Flächensickerung *f*; flächenhafter
Wasseraustritt *m*

2723 SURFACE SPREADING
method of artificial recharge of
water by spreading on surface
f épandage *m* en surface
d Flächenberieselung *f*

2724 SURFACE TENSION
free specific surface energy
occurring at the interface between
a liquid and its own vapor phase
f tension *f* superficielle
d Oberflächenspannung *f*

2725 SURFACE WATER
water obtained from surface
supplies
f eau *f* de surface
d Oberflächenwasser *n*

2726 SURFACE WATER SUPPLY
f alimentation *f* en eau de surface
d Oberflächenwasservorräte *mpl*

2727 SURGING
rapid upward and downward movem
of a plunger in a well (development
method)

f   décolmatage *m* d'un puits
d   Stöpseln *n* eines Brunnens

2728   SURVEY
f   levé *m*
d   Vermessung *f*

SURVEY, dipmeter see 511
-, field see 718
-, magnetic see 1179
-, resistivity see 2401

2729   SURVEYING
f   arpentage *m*
d   Vermessung *f*; Landvermessung *f*

2730   SUSPENDED LOAD
sedimentary matter transported
in suspension by a moving stream
f   charge *f* en suspension
d   Schwebefrachtung *f*;
    Schwebstoffbelastung *f*

2731   SUSPENDED MATTER
solid matter small enough to be held
in suspension by moving or stagnant
water
f   matière *f* en suspension
d   Schwebstoff *m*

SUSPENDED SUBSURFACE WATER
see vadose water

2732   SUSPENDED WATER
water in zone of aeration kept in
suspension by capillary forces
f   eau *f* de suspension
d   Wasser *n* in der luftbeeinflussten
    Zone; schwebendes Wasser *n*

2733   SUSTAINED YIELD
rate at which water can be with-
drawn from an aquifer without
depleting the supply
f   débit *m* permanent
d   Dauerspende *f*

2734   SWALE
marshy depression or depression in
groundmoraine
f   mare *f*
d   Grundmoränetümpel *m*

2735   SWELLING
volume increase due to intake and
absorption of water (especially
clays)
f   gonflement *m*
d   Quellen *n*; Anschwellen *n*

SWELLING, soil see 2600

2736   SWELLING RATE
time rate of volume increase
f   vitesse *f* de gonflement
d   Anschwellrate *f*

2737   SWIVEL
rotating head of drillstem through
which the drilling fluid is injected
f   tête *f* d'injection
d   Bohrkopf *m*

2738   SYENITE
igneous rock with no quartz
content
f   syénite *f*
d   Syenit *m*

2739   SYNCLINAL VALLEY
valley following the axis of a
syncline
f   vallée *f* synclinale
d   Muldental *n*

2740   SYNCLINE
downfolded stratum
f   synclinal *m*
d   Mulde *f*

2741   SYNOPTIC NETWORK
network of first order stations
permitting the regular observation
of weather for all points at the
same time
f   réseau *m* synoptique
d   synoptisches Beobachtungsnetz *n*

2742   SYNTHETIC UNIT HYDROGRAPH
unit hydrograph constructed by
assuming reaction of a drainage
basin based on its physical
characteristics
f   hydrogramme *m* unitaire synthétique
d   synthetische Einheitskurve *f*
    der Abflussganglinie; theoretischer
    Einheitshydrograph *m*

SYSTEM, drainage see 558
-, open see 2132
-, river see 2423
-, rock see 2430
-, supply see 2709
-, well point see 2998

T

TABLE, permafrost see 2201
-, rotating see 2439
-, water see 2962

2743 TABLE MOUNTAIN
flat topped mountain; mesa
f montagne f tabulaire
d Tafelberg m

2744 TAILWATER
lower course of a river with
respect to a given point or structure
f cours m inférieur; eau f d'aval
d Unterlauf m; Unterwasser n

2745 TALC
soft silica rock containing
magnesium
f talc m
d Talk m

2746 TALUS CONE
conelike collecyion of disintegrated
rock material originating from and
adjacent to a steeper slope
f cône m de déjection
d Schuttkegel m

2747 TALUS FAN
f cône m d'alluvions
d Schuttfächer m

TANK, air separating see 46
-, gage see 805
-, holding see 939

2748 TAPE GAGE
f ruban m de mesure; décamètre m
en ruban
d Messband n; Bandmasspegel m

2749 TAPPING WELL
well completed at top of aquifer (no
penetration)
f puits m imparfait effleurant la
nappe
d unvollkommener Brunnen m
(nur bis zur Grundwasserdeck-
fläche vordringend)

2750 TECTONIC
pertaining to structural features
due to the deformation of the crust
f tectonique
d tektonisch

2751 TECTONIC VALLEY
valley formed by tectonic forces
f vallée f structurale
d tektonisches Tal n

2752 TELEMETERING
method of transmitting measurements
from point of measure to a distant
reading or recording device
f télémesure f
d Fernmessung f

TEMPERATURE, formation see 779

2753 TEMPERATURE EFFICIENCY
efficiency factor defined by
Thornthwaite for different climates
f efficacité f de température
d Temperaturwirksamkeit f

2754 TEMPERATURE LOG
recording of curve of groundwater
temperature in a well
f diagraphie f de température
d Temperaturlog n

2755 TEMPORARY CASING
f tubage m temporaire
d vorläufige Verrohrung f

2756 TEMPORARY HARDNESS
carbonate hardners
f dureté f temporaire; dureté f
carbonatée
d vorübergehende Härte f;
temporäre Härte f

TENSION, interfacial see 1059
-, soil moisture see 2594
-, surface see 2724

2757 TENSILE STRENGTH
f résistance f à la traction
d Zugfestigkeit f

TENSOR, permeability see 2207

2758 TENSOR QUANTITY
f quantité f tensorielle
d Tensorgrösse f

TERMINAL, ground see 891

2759 TERMINAL MORAINE
glacial deposit accumulated in front
of glacier

f   moraine f frontale
d   Endmoräne f

2760   TERRACE
flat surface bounded by steplike
steep slopes
f   terrasse f
d   Terrasse f; Absatz m

TERRACE, fill see 722
-, river see 2424
-, rock see 2431
-, strath see 2657

2761   TERRANE
area with some specific characteristics (e.g. limestone terrane)
f   terrain m
d   Gelände n

2762   TERTIARY
geologic period of the Cenozoic era
f   Ère f Tertiaire
d   Tertiär n

TEST, field see 719
-, infiltrometer see 1030
-, model see 2061
-, pumping see 2308

2763   TEST HOLE
hole to test depth of ground water,
water quality or geological
conditions; exploratory drillhole
f   puits m d'essai; sondage m d'essai
d   Versuchsbohrung f;
    Untersuchungsbohrung f;
    Testbohrung f

2764   TEST PIT
f   fouille f de recherche
d   Schürfloch n

TEXTURE, rock see 2432

2765   TEXTURE OF SOIL
f   texture f de sol
d   Bodentextur f

2766   THALWEG
line of maximum depth of stream
cross section
f   thalweg m; talweg m
d   Talweg m

2767   THEIS EQUATION
nonequilibrium equation of radial
flow towards well
f   équation f de Theis
d   Theis'sche Brunnengleichung f

2768   THERMAL CONDUCTIVITY
f   conductibilité f thermique
d   Wärmeleitfähigkeit f

2769   THERMAL SPRING
spring with temperature of spring
water above average temperature
of superficial rock
f   source f thermale
d   Thermalquelle f

2770   THERMAL STRATIFICATION
stratification of water in reservoirs
due to thermal-density differences
f   stratification f thermique
d   Wärmeschichtung f;
    Temperaturschichtung f

2771   THERMOCLINE
intermediate layer in stratified water
f   thermocline m
d   Sprungschicht f

2772   THERMOCOUPLE
temperature measuring device
based on proportionality between
thermoelectric current and temperature
difference between thermojunctions
f   thermocouple m
d   Thermoelement n

2773   THERMOMETER
f   thermomètre m
d   Thermometer n

THERMOMETER, resistance see
2396

2774   THICKNESS
width of a bed
f   épaisseur f; puissance f d'une
    couche
d   Mächtigkeit f; Schichtmächtigkeit

2775   THIEF ZONE
zone through which drilling fluid is
lost into formation through borehole
wall
f   zone f de perte de boue
d   Verlustzone f; Diebszone f

2776   THIEM EQUATION
equation describing steady state
equilibrium radial flow into well
f   formule f de Thiem
d   Thiem'sche Brunnenformel f

2777   THIXOTROPY
property of a gel to become fluid
under application of shear stresses

f thixotropie *f*
d Thixotropie *f*

2778 THREADED JOINT
f joint *m* fileté
d Gewindeverbinder *m*

2779 THRESHOLD SATURATION
saturation below which no flow
occurs
f saturation *f* de seuil
d Schwellensättigungswert *m*

2780 THROTTLE VALVE
f clapet *m* étrangleur
d Drosselventil *n*

2781 THROUGHFALL
part of precipitation that reaches
ground by falling through vegetative
cover
f pluie *f* tombant directement sur
le sol (à travers le feuillage)
d Tropfendurchfall *m*

2782 THROW
vertical displacement of stratum
along a fault plane
f rejet *m* vertical
d seigere Sprunghöhe *f*

2783 TIDAL CURRENT
current produced by tidal action
f courant *m* de marée
d Gezeitenstrom *m*

2784 TIDAL EFFICIENCY
ratio of piezometric level amplitude
to tidal amplitude
f coefficient *m* de fluctuation par
marées
d Gezeitenwirkungsgrad *m*

2785 TIDAL FLUCTUATION
fluctuation of water level due to
tidal motion
f fluctuation *f* dûe aux marées
d Gezeitenschwankung *f*

2786 TIDAL RIVER
river strongly influenced and
subject to tidal currents
f rivière *f* à marées
d Tidefluss *m*

2787 TIGHTEST PACKING
arrangement of particles
allowing only minimum void space
in unit cell of sample
f arrangement *m* le plus compact;
empilement *m* le plus serré
d dichteste Packung *f*

TILE, drain see 559

2788 TILE PIPE
f tuyau *m* en terre cuite
d Dränagerohr *n*; Tonrohr *n*

2789 TILL
glacial deposit
f argile *m* à blocaux; depôt *m*
glacial
d Geschiebemergel *m*

TILL, glacial see 849
-, lodgement see 1162

2790 TILTED AQUIFER
dipping aquifer, inclined aquifer
f nappe *f* aquifère inclinée
d einfallender Grundwasserleiter *m*

TIME, arrival see 112
-, lag see 1119
-, transit see 2821
-, travel see 2821

2791 TIME BASE
sum of storm duration time and
concentration time in hydrograph
f temps *m* de base
d Basiszeit *f*

2792 TIME-DRAWDOWN CURVE
plot of drawdown variation with time
f courbe *f* rabattement-temps
d Absenkungsganglinie *f*

2793 TIME LAG
time elapsed between the onset of a
certain event and the reaction to this
event
f retard *m*
d Verzögerung *f*; Verspätung *f*

2794 TIME OF CONCENTRATION
time required for surface runoff
produced in farthest part of basin
to reach concentration point under
consideration
f temps *m* de concentration
d Konzentrationszeit *f*

2795 TIME OF RISE
time between first arrival of runoff
and arrival of the peak flow
f temps *m* de montée
d Steigdauer *f*

2796 TIMER
time indicator
f minuterie *f*
d Zeitzähler *m*

2797 TIPPING BUCKET
revolving measuring reservoirs
in a recording rain gage
f auget *m* basculeur
d Wippe *f*; Hornersche Wippe *f*

TOOL, cable see 220
-, fishing see 731
- standard see 2641

2798 TOOL BODY
main body of a drilling tool on
which cutting edges are mounted
f matrice *f* d'outil
d Meisselkörper *m*

2799 TOOL JOINT
drill pipe connection
f joint *m* de tige
d Gestängeverbinder *m*

2800 TOPOGRAPHIC DIVIDE
crest line dividing one drainage
basin from another
f ligne *f* de partage topographique
d topographische Wasserscheide *f*

2801 TOPOGRAPHY
physical features of a geographical
area
f topographie *f*
d Topographie *f*; Lagebeschreibung *f*

2802 TOPSOIL
topmost portion of soil profile
f couverture *f* de sol
d Mutterboden *m*

2803 TORSION
f torsion *f*
d Torsion *f*; Verdrehung *f*;
Verdrillung *f*

2804 TORSION BALANCE
f balance *f* de torsion
d Torsionswaage *f*; Drehwaage *f*

2805 TORTUOSITY
ratio of actual length of pore
channel to over all length of sample;
sinuosity of actual flow path in
porous medium
f tortuosité *f*
d Tortuosität *f*

2806 TOTAL CAPACITY
maximum rate of yield of a well
f débit *m* maximum
d maximale Schüttung *f*

2807 TOTAL HARDNESS
sum of permanent and temporary
hardness
f dureté *f* totale
d Gesamthärte *f*

2808 TOTAL PORE SPACE
sum of interconnected and non-
interconnected pore space
f volume *m* total des pores
d Gesamtporenvolumen *n*;
Gesamtporenraum *m*

2809 TOTAL POROSITY
see absolute porosity
f porosité *f* totale
d totale Porosität *f*

2810 TOTAL RUNOFF
sum of all components of runoff
into a stream
f écoulement *m* total
d Gesamtabfluss *m*

2811 TOURMALINE
borosilicate mineral
f tourmaline *f*
d Turmalin *m*

TRACE, pen see 2189

2812 TRACE CONSTITUENTS
f constituant *m* en trace
d Spurenelement *n*; Spuren-
bestandteil *n*

2813 TRACE ELEMENT
f élément *m* en trace
d Spurenelement *n*

2814 TRACER
substance introduced into a flow
system at a very low concentration
for the observation of velocity
patterns
f traceur *m*
d Indikator *m*

TRACER, radioactive see 2323

2815 TRACER FLOW METHOD
method of determining flow
velocities and directions by intro-
ducing tracers or indicators into
ground water stream
f méthode *f* des traceurs
d Tracerverfahren *n*;
Immissionsverfahren *n*

TRACTION LOAD, see bed boad

2816 TRANQUIL FLOW
open channel flow with Froude
number smaller than unity
f écoulement m tranquille
d ruhige Strömung f

2817 TRANSDUCER
f transducteur m
d Geber m

TRANSFER, energy see 653
-, heat see 928
-, mass see 1195

2818 TRANSGRESSION
spreading of the sea over level
areas
f transgression f
d Transgression f

2819 TRANSITION
f transition f
d Übergang m

2820 TRANSITION ZONE
zone in which properties of two
adjacent units change gradually
f zone f de transition
d Übergangszone f

2821 TRANSIT TIME;
TRAVEL TIME
travel time of a sonic impulse
through a given length of rock
f temps m de propagation;
temps m de parcours; durée f de
parcours
d Laufzeit f

2822 TRANSMISSION
f transmission f
d Durchleitung f; Weiterleitung f

2823 TRANSMISSION CAPACITY
property of porous medium to
conduct fluid
f capacité f de transmission
d Leitvermögen n

2824 TRANSMISSIVITY;
COEFFICIENT OF TRANS-
MISSIBILITY
product of coefficient of
permeability and thickness of
aquifer
f transmissivité f
d Einheitsergiebigkeit f

2825 TRANSPIRATION
evaporation of water absorbed by
plants
f transpiration f
d Transpiration f; Pflanzen-
verdunstung f

TRANSPIRATION, cuticular see 430
-, stomatal see 2649

2826 TRANSPIRATION DEPTH
depth of water consumed annually
by plants
f hauteur f de transpiration
d Transpirationshöhe f

2827 TRANSPIRATION RATIO
ratio of water weight transpired to
weight of dry matter produced
(exclusive of roots)
f coefficient m de transpiration
d Transpirationskoeffizient m

2828 TRANSPORTATIONAL PROCESS
all processes contributing to the
transport of eroded material
f procédé m de transport
d Verfrachtung f; Transport-
vorgang m

2829 TRANSVERSE PERMEABILITY
permeability measured perpendicular
to axis of core sample
f perméabilité f transversale
d quergerichtete Permeabilität f

2830 TRANSVERSE WAVE
wave generated by shearing displace-
ments where wave motion is perpend-
ular to direction of propagation
f onde f de cisaillement
d Scherungswelle f

TRAVEL TIME, see transit time

2831 TRAVERTINE
porous calcium carbonate
concretionary deposit
f travertin m
d Travertin m

2832 TREE MOLD
hollow mold left by a tree trunk in
a lava flow
f eisomorphose f
d Baumgussform f; Lavamatrix f

2833 TRELLIS
geometrical arrangement of inter-
woven pattern

f   treillis *m*
d   Flechtmuster *n*

2834   TRELLIS DRAINAGE PATTERN
arrangement of stream and
tributaries in a rectangular fashion
f   configuration *f* en espalier
d   gitterförmige Anordnung *f*

2835   TREMOLITE
silicate mineral of the amphibole
group
f   trémolite *m*
d   Tremolit *m*

2836   TRIASSIC
oldest geologic period of the
Mesozoic era
f   Trias *m*
d   Trias *n*

2837   TRIBUTARY
stream contributing its waters to
another stream of higher order
f   tributaire *m*; affluent *m*
d   Nebenfluss *m*

2838   TRIBUTARY RIVER
smaller stream entering and
contributing to flow of a bigger
river
f   affluent *m*
d   Nebenfluss *m*

2839   TRIBUTARY VALLEY
less important valley joining bigger
valley
f   vallée *f* tributaire
d   Seitental *n*

2840   TRICKLING
f   ruissellement *m*
d   Rinnsal *n*

2841   TRICONE ROCK BIT
rotary drilling bit with three
cone shaped rollers
f   tricône *m*
d   Dreirollenmeissel *m*

2842   TRIPLE POINT
point at which solid, liquid and
vapor phase are in equilibrium
f   point *m* triple
d   Tripelpunkt *m*

2843   TRIPOLY
very fine grained silica sand
f   tripoli *m*
d   Kieselgur *m*

2844   TRITIUM
isotope of water H_3O (HTO) of
special usefulness in hydrologic
tracer studies
f   tritium *m*
d   Tritium *n*

2845   TROUGH
surface depression
f   dépression *f*; bassin *m*
d   Trog *m*; Senke *f*; Mulde *f*

2846   TRUCK-MOUNTED
f   mobile
d   fahrbar

2847   TRUE VELOCITY
in ground water flow: velocity in
porous interstice; interstitial
velocity
f   vitesse *f* interstitielle;
    vitesse *f* dans les pores
d   Porenfliessgeschwindigkeit *f*;
    Bahngeschwindigkeit *f*

2848   TRUNCATION
horizontal or vertical clean cut of
a topographic feature
f   rabotage *m*
d   Abschleifung *f*

TUBE, lava see 1140
-, measuring see 2013

2849   TUBULAR SPRING
spring issuing from round channel
such as a lava tube
f   source *f* tubulaire
d   Rundnischenquelle *f*

2850   TUFF
porous rock formed by compaction
of volcanic ashes
f   tuf *m*
d   Tuff *m*

2851   TURBIDITY
diminishing of light penetration
through water sample due to
suspended and colloidal materials
f   trouble *m*; turbidité *f*
d   Trübung *f*

2852   TURBINE PUMP
f   pompe *f* à turbine
d   Turbinenpumpe *f*

TURBINE PUMP, deep well
see 449

2853   TURBODRILL
       drill where rotary movement is
       generated in a turbine directly
       above the bit
       f   turboforeuse *f*
       d   Bohrturbine *f*

2854   TURBULENCE
       irregular motion of fluid particles
       in an inertia dominated flow
       regimen

       f   turbulence *f*
       d   Turbulenz *f*

2855   TYPE CURVE
       plot of well function versus lower
       limit of integral used in Theis'
       graphical solution method
       f   courbe *f* standard
       d   Bezugskurve *f* der Brunnen-
           funktion W(u)

U

2856 UNALTERED ROCK
rock that has not experienced
physical or chemical erosion
f roche f saine
d gewachsener Fels m

2857 UNCASED HOLE
f puits m ouvert
d unverrohrte Bohrung f

2858 UNCONFINED FLOW
flow displaying free surface
f écoulement m en nappe libre
d ungespannter Grundwasserfluss m

2859 UNCONFINED WATER
ground water vertically in direct
contact with atmosphere
f eau f libre; nappe f libre
d ungespanntes Grundwasser n;
freies Grundwasser n

2860 UNCONFORMITY
fossil land surface representing
absence of a sequence of sediments
f discontinuité f stratigraphique
d Diskordanz f; Schichtlücke f

2861 UNCONFORMITY SPRING
spring issuing at contact of
aquifer with an unconformity
f source f de faille
d Verwerfungsquelle f

2862 UNCONTAMINATED ZONE
in electrical logging practice zone
around borehole not contaminated
by mud filtrate
f zone f non-contaminée
d unberührte Zone f

2863 UNDERDRAINAGE
drainage from under a hydrologic
feature such as river, barrier,
lake etc.
f infradrainage m
d Unterströmung f

2864 UNDERGROUND WATERS
subsurface waters, waters below
the ground
f eaux f pl souterraines
d unterirdische Wässer n pl

2865 UNIFORM
f uniforme
d einheitlich; gleichmässig

2866 UNIFORM FLOW
flow with constant velocity at all
points and at all times
f écoulement m uniforme
d gleichförmige Strömung f

UNCONFORMITY, angular see 81

2867 UNIFORMITY COEFFICIENT
ratio of the 60 percentile grain
size to the 10 percentile, indicating
degree of sorting of granular
material; (Hazen uniformity
coefficient)
f coefficient m d'uniformité
d Gleichförmigkeitsziffer f
(nach Hazen)

UNIT, geohydrologic see 826
-, pumping see 2309

2868 UNIT-HYDROGRAPH
hypothetical discharge hydrograph
for a given point resulting from
unit rainfall which produces unit
runoff
f hydrogramme m unitaire
d Einheitskurve f der Abflussganglinie; Einheitshydrograph m

2869 UNSATURATED COEFFICIENT OF
PERMEABILITY
apparent coefficient of permeability
in flow through an unsaturated medium
f coefficient m de perméabilité
relative
d relativer Durchlässigkeitsbeiwert m
ungesättigte Durchlässigkeitsziffer f

2870 UNSATURATED FLOW
two phase flow through pores only
partially filled with water and air
f écoulement m en régime non-
saturé
d Strömung f in der belüfteten
Zone; ungesättigter Fluss m

2871 UNSTEADY FLOW
flow with finite local acceleration
term; streamlines vary with time
f écoulement m non-permanent
d unstetige Strömung f

2872 UPLIFT
relative upward movement of a part
of the earth's crust

f   soulèvement *m*
d   Erhebung *f*; Hebung *f*

2873   UPPER CONFINING BED
       impermeable bed overlying
       an aquifer
       f   toit *m* imperméable d'un
           aquifère
       d   Deckschicht *f*

2874   UPSTREAM
       f   en amont
       d   flussaufwärts

USE, conjuctive see 356
-, consumptive see 363
-, water see 2963

2875   U.S. WEATHER BUREAU CLASS
       A LAND PAN
       evaporimeter developed by U.S.
       Weather Bureau, recommended as
       standard device by the World
       Meteorological Organization
       f   bac *m* de classe A
       d   Landkessel A *m* (Standardgerät)

V

2876 VADOSE WATER;
SUSPENDED SUBSURFACE WATER
water suspended in the unsaturated
zone of aeration between surface
waters and ground water
f   eaux *f pl* suspendues; eaux *f pl*
vadoses
d   vadoses Grundwasser *n*;
schwebendes Grundwasser *n*

2877 VALLEY
f   vallée *f*
d   Tal *n*

VALLEY, anticlinal see 92
-, antecedent see 91
-, buried see 212
-, rift see 2410
-, strike see 2675
-, superimposed see 2706
-, synclinal see 2739
-, tectonic see 2751
-, tributary see 2839

2878 VALLEY FILL
unconsolidated debris accumulated
on the valley bottom
f   remblaiement *m* de vallée
d   Talschutt *m*

2879 VALLEYSIDE-SLOPE
f   versant *m* d'une vallée
d   Talhang *m*

2880 VALLEY SPRING
springs occurring at valley sides
where water table intersects
surface
f   source *f* de vallée
d   Talquelle *f*

VALUE, discrete see 522
-, limiting see 1153
-, mean see 2005

2881 VALVE
f   vanne *f*
d   Ventil *n*

VALVE, air release 45
-, ball see 135
-, butterfly see 214
-, check see 283
-, control see 378
-, drain see 560

VALVE, foot see 774
-, gate see 822
-, safety see 2448
-, throttle see 2780

2882 VAPORIZATION
process by which liquid or solid
water changes into gaseous state
f   vaporisation *f*
d   Verdampfung *f*

2883 VAPOR PRESSURE (SATURATION......)
f   pression *f* de vapeur
d   Dampfdruck *m*

2884 VARIANCE
square of standard deviation
f   variance *f*
d   Streuung *f*

2885 VARVE
alternating coarse and fine
grained layer in glacial lake
sediments
f   varve *f*
d   Warve *f*

2886 VECTOR FIELD
f   champ *m* vectoriel
d   Vektorfeld *n*

2887 VEGETATION COVER
cover of living vegetation on top
of upper soil horizon
f   couverture *f* végétale
d   Pflanzendecke *f*

2888 VEIN
opening filled with mineral matter
f   filon *m*
d   Gang *m*

2889 VELOCITY
f   vitesse *f*
d   Geschwindigkeit *f*

VELOCITY, Darcy see 440
-, field... of groundwater see 720
-, rising see 2416
-, seepage see 440, 2502
-, settling see 2518
-, shear see 2530
-, sound see 2611
-, true see 2847
-, wave see 2972

2890 VELOCITY HEAD
f énergie *f* cinétique
d Geschwindigkeitshöhe *f*

2891 VELOCITY POTENTIAL
f potentiel *m* de vélocité
d Geschwindigkeitspotential *n*

2892 VERNIER
part of measuring device to obtain
very fine adjustment
f vernier *m*
d Nonius *m*

2893 VERY FINE SAND
grain diameter 0.1 to 0.05 mm
(USBS)
f sable *m* très fin
d Feinstsand *m*

2894 VESICULAR
containing small circular cavities
f vésiculeux
d bläschenförmig

2895 VIRGIN FLOW
flow unaffected by artificial
diversions, impoundments, or
channels
f écoulement *m* vierge
d unbeeinflusste Strömung *f*

2896 VISCOSIMETER
f viscosimètre *m*
d Viskosimeter *n*

2897 VISCOSITY
resistance of liquid to flow; property
of a real fluid creating shear
forces between two fluid elements
and giving rise to fluid friction
f viscosité *f*
d Viskosität *f*; Zähigkeit *f*

2898 VISCOUS FORCE
f force *f* de viscosité
d Reibungskraft *f*

2899 VOID RATIO
ratio of volume of voids to volume
of solids in a porous sample
f indice *m* des vides
d relativer Porenraum *m*

2900 VOIDS
open space between solid material
in a porous medium
f vides *mpl*
d Hohlräume *mpl*

2901 VOLATILE COMPONENTS
f composants *mpl* volatils
d flüchtige Bestandteile *mpl*

2902 VOLCANIC ACTIVITY
igneous activity near or at the
surface of the earth with outflow
of the igneous material on the
surface
f activité *f* volcanique;
volcanisme *m*
d Vulkanismus *m* (im engeren
Sinne)

2903 VOLCANIC ASH
fine grained material resulting
from explosion of magma
f cendre *f* volcanique
d Vulkanasche *f*

2904 VOLCANIC LAKE
lake formed in the impermeable
part of a volcanic crater
f lac *m* volcanique
d Vulkansee *m*; Mar *n*

2905 VOLCANIC VENT
chimney like conduit from body of
magma to the place of eruption
f diatrème *m*; évent *m*
d Vulkanschlot *m*

2906 VOLCANIC WATER
water in or derived from shallow
magma
f eaux *fpl* volcaniques
d vulkanisches Wasser *n*

2907 VOLTMETER
f voltmètre *m*
d Spannungsmesser *m*; Voltmeter

VOLUME, solid see 2605
-, specific see 2621

2908 VOLUMETRIC FLOWMETER
apparatus to measure volume flow
rate
f débimètre *m* volumétrique
d Volumenflussmessgerät *n*

2909 VOLUMETRIC MOISTURE CONTE.
concentration of water in soil by
volume
f teneur *f* en eau par volume
d volumetrischer Feuchtegehalt *m*

2910   VUGULAR PORE SPACE
       void space due to solution cavities
       of small size
       f   espace *m* des vides par solution
       d   Lösungshohlraum *m*

W

2911 WADING MEASUREMENT
discharge measurement during
which hydrographer can take
readings standing in the river
f jaugeage *m* à gué
d Furtmessung *f*

2912 WALKING BEAM
oscillating beam used to produce
the rise and fall of the tools in
cable-tool drilling
f balancier *m*
d Bohrschwengel *m*

2913 WALL OF A WELL
f paroi *f* d'un puits
d Bohrlochswand *f*

2914 WARM SPRING
f source *f* chaude
d Arkatotherme *f*

2915 WASH
small ravine due to outwash by
flow in desert regions
f oued *m*
d Wadi *m*

2916 WASHER
f rondelle *f*
d Unterlegscheibe *f*

2917 WASH LOAD
incoming load of suspended
sediment passing through river
network without depositing
f charge *f* de ruissellement
d eingeleitete Materialfrachtung *f*

2918 WASHOVER
liberating a stuck tool by drilling
over it with an overshot
f surforage *m*
d Überbohren *n*

2919 WASTE DISPOSAL
f élimination *f* des résidus
d Abfallbeseitigung *f*

2920 WASTE LOAD
content of wastes by weight of
volume transported by or discharged into a river
f charge *f* en résidus
d Abwasserlast *f*

2921 WASTE PRODUCTS
f déchets *mpl*
d Abfälle *mpl*; Abfallstoffe *mpl*

2922 WASTE WATER
water containing sewage and waste
products
f eaux *fpl* d'égouts
d Abwasser *n*

2923 WATER
f eau *f*
d Wasser *n*

WATER, active see 22
-, available see 124
-, backwash see 131
-, brackish see 199
-, capillary see 243
-, cavern see 263
-, compensation see 328
-, confined see 349
-, connate see 357
-, cooling see 384
-, dead see 443
-, drinking see 586
-, flood see 751
-, fresh see 791
-, gravitational see 878
-, head see 924
-, hygroscopic see 992
-, imported see 1008
-, industrial see 1021
-, infiltration see 1028
-, interstitial see 1069
-, intrapermafrost see 1070
-, juvenile see 1103
-, low see 1174
-, magmatic see 1178
-, marine see 1187
-, metamorphic see 2033
-, meteoric see 2034
-, mine see 2049
-, natural see 2103
-, oceanic see 2124
-, oil field see 2125
-, pellicular see 2183
-, phreatic see 2220
-, plutonic see 2252
-, polluted see 2261
-, ponded see 2265
-, potable see 2274
-, raw see 2345
-, recharge see 2360
-, resurgent see 2402

WATER, saline see 2452
-, salty see 2459
-, soil see 2601
-, subsiding see 2687
-, subpermafrost see 2685
-, suprapermafrost see 2710
-, surface see 2725
-, suspended see 2732
-, suspended subsurface see 2876
-, unconfined see 2859
-, vadose see 2876
-, volcanic see 2906
-, waste see 2922
-, well see 3005

2924 WATER-BALANCE
instrument to measure evaporation
by gravimetry (developed by Wild)
f évaporomètre m (de Wild)
d Verdunstungswaage f (nach
Wild)

2925 WATER-BEARING
containing water
f aquifère
d wasserhaltig; wasserführend

2926 WATER-BORNE DISEASE
disease spread by organic contaminants contained in the water supply
f maladie f d'origine hydrique
d Wasserkrankheit f

2927 WATER BUDGET
quantitative accounting of water
volumes involved in hydrologic
cycle
f bilan m hydrologique
d Wasserbilanz f

2928 WATER CATCHMENT
intake of water from an aquifer or
a surface reservoir
f puisage m d'eau; captage m d'eau
d Wasserfassung f; Wasserge-
winnung f

2929 WATER CONSERVATION
all measures to reduce quantitative
or qualitative spoilage of water
f conservation f d'eau
d Wasserbewirtschaftung f

2930 WATER CONTENT
f teneur f en eau
d Wassergehalt m

2931 WATER COURSE
any channel conveying water
f cours m d'eau
d Wasserlauf m

WATER COURSE, receiving see
2351

2932 WATER CYCLE
f cycle m d'eau
d Wasserkreislauf m

2933 WATER DEMAND
f besoin m en eau
d Wasserbedarf m

2934 WATER EQUIVALENT
depth of water resulting from
melting of snow
f hauteur f d'eau équivalente
d Wasserwert m des Schnees

2935 WATER GAGING
f hydrométrie f
d Wassermessung f

2936 WATER HAMMER
abnormally high pressure rise in a
pipe when sudden changes in flow
occur
f coup m de bélier
d hydraulischer Stoss m;
Wasserhammer m

2937 WATER INVASION
sudden invasion of water into well
or bore
f invasion f d'eau
d Wassereinbruch m

2938 WATER LAW
f législation f des eaux
d Wasserrecht n

2939 WATER LEVEL
level of free surface of a water
body or water column
f niveau m d'eau
d Wasserspiegel m

2940 WATERLOGGED
water saturated
f noyé
d durchtränkt

2941 WATERLOGGING
water accummulation on top of
soil where water table and ground
surface coincide
f imbibition f d'eau (sous forme
de marais)
d Wasserdurchtränkung f

2942 WATER METER
f compteur m d'eau
d Wasseruhr f

2943 WATER OF CONSTITUTION
      chemically bound water
      f eau *f* de constitution
      d Konstitutionswasser *n*

2944 WATER OF CRYSTALLIZATION
      water embodied in crystal structure
      f eau *f* de cristallisation
      d Kristallisationswasser *n*

2945 WATER OF DEHYDRATION
      water freed from hydrous
      minerals by chemical changes
      f eau *f* de constitution
      d Dehydrationswasser *n*;
         Konstitutionswasser *n*

2946 WATER PIPE
      f conduite *f* d'eau
      d Wasserleitung *f*

2947 WATER PUMPAGE
      f élévation *f* de l'eau;
         pompage *m* de l'eau
      d Wasserhebung *f*

2948 WATER QUALITY
      physical chemical and biological
      characteristics of water
      f propriétés *fpl* caractéristiques
         de l'eau
      d Wasserbeschaffenheit *f*;
         Wassergüte *f*

2949 WATER RECLAMATION
      process waste water purification
      to acceptable standards for further
      use
      f récupération *f* d'eau
      d Wasserrückgewinnung *f*;
         Abwasserrückgewinnung *f*

2950 WATER REQUIREMENT
      quantity of water needed for crop
      regardless of source
      f demande *f* en eau
      d Wasserbedarf *m*

2951 WATER RESOURCES
      total supply of surface ground and
      reclaimed water that can be used
      f ressources *fpl* en eau
      d Wasservorräte *mpl*;
         Wasserschatz *m*

2952 WATER RESOURCES
      MANAGEMENT
      f économie *f* des eaux
      d Wasserwirtschaft *f*

      WATER RETAINING
      see specific retention

      WATERS, underground see 2864

2953 WATER SAMPLE
      f échantillon *m* d'eau
      d Wasserprobe *f*

2954 WATER SEPARATOR
      f séparateur d'eau *m*
      d Wasserabscheider *m*

2955 WATERSHED
      a) drainage basin;
      b) divide separating one drainage
         basin from another
      f a) bassin *m* hydrologique
         b) ligne *f* de partage
      d a) Einzugsgebiet *n*
         b) Wasserscheide *f*

2956 WATER SHORTAGE
      f pénurie *f* d'eau
      d Wassermangel *m*

2957 WATER SOLUBLE
      f soluble dans l'eau
      d wasserlöslich

2958 WATER STAGE
      height of the water level
      f hauteur *f* d'eau
      d Wasserstand *m*

2959 WATER-STAGE RECORDER
      f limnigraphe *m*
      d Schreibpegel *m*

2960 WATER SUPPLY
      f alimentation *f* en eau;
         approvisionnement *m* en eau
      d Wasserversorgung *f*;
         Wasserdarbietung *f*

2961 WATER SURFACE SLOPE
      see also hydraulic gradient for
      free surface waters
      f pente *f* de la ligne d'eau
      d Wasserspiegelgefälle *n*

2962 WATER TABLE
      surface separating ground water
      zone from capillary fringe in
      unconfined aquifer conditions
      f niveau *m* phréatique; surface *f*
         hydrostatique; surface *f* libre
         des eaux souterraines
      d Grundwasserspiegel *m*;
         Grundwasseroberfläche *f*

WATER TABLE perched see 2191

2963 WATER USE
f utilisation f de l'eau
d Wassernutzung f

2964 WATER VAPOR
f vapeur f d'eau
d Wasserdampf m

2965 WATERWAY
artificial or natural watercourse
fit for navigation
f canal m; cours m d'eau
d Wasserweg m

WATER WITCHING, see dowsing

2966 WATER WORKS
plant where water is treated and
prepared for municipal consumption
f usine f d'eau
d Wasserwerk n

2967 WATER YEAR
12 month period for streamflow
computation (adopted by U.S.
Geological Survey, Oct. 1 to Sept. 30)
f année f hydrologique
d hydrologisches Jahr n

2968 WATER-YIELD
f débit m d'exploitation
d Wasserspende f; Wasserergiebig-
keit f

WAVE, compression see 334
-, flood see 752
-, longitudinal see 1169
-, seismic see 2506
-, shear see 2531
-, shock see 2537
-, transverse see 2830

2969 WAVE FRONT
f front m d'onde
d Wellenfront f

2970 WAVE PATH
f trajectoire f des ondes;
rayon m
d Wellenweg m

2971 WAVE PROPAGATION
f propagation f des ondes
d Wellenausbreitung f

2972 WAVE VELOCITY
f célérité f d'une onde
d Wellengeschwindigkeit f

2973 WEAR RESISTANCE
f résistance f à l'usure
d Verschleissfestigkeit f

2974 WEATHERING
disintegration and decomposition of
rocks by different geological
processes
f altération f des roches
d Verwitterung f

2975 WEATHER MODIFICATION
f modification f artificielle du
temps
d künstliche Wetterbeeinflussung f

2976 WEDGE STORAGE
storage in form of a wedge
overlying prism; storage in flooded
river segment
f stockage m en forme de coin
d keilförmige Fallwasserspeicherung f

2977 WEIGHING FACTOR
f coefficient m de pondération
d Gewichtszahl f

WEIGHT, bit see 182

2978 WEIGHT DENSITY
f poids m spécifique
d Wichte f; spezifisches Gewicht n

2979 WEIR
dam across a water course to
control, raise or measure water
flow
f déversoir m
d Wehr n

WEIR, measuring see 2014

2980 WEIR COEFFICIENT
coefficient used in transforming
water depths into discharge volumes
in weir measurements
f coefficient m du déversoir
d Wehrbeiwert m

2981 WELDED JOINT
f joint m soudé
d Schweissverbindung f

WELL, abandonded see 1
--, absorbing see 8
-, artesian see 115
-, collector see 325
-, diffusion see 2361
-, disposal see 527
-, draw see 564

WELL, driven see 591
-, dug see 605
-, eccentric see 618
-, failing see 701
-, flowing artesian see 756
-, gage see 806
-, image see 1000
-, inverted see 2361
-, jetted see 1098
-, multiaquifer see 2094
-, observation see 2121
-, oil see 2127
-, partially penetrated see 2172
-, permanent see 2204
-, reamed see 2346
-, recharge see 2361
-, shallow see 2524
-, stilling see 2648
-, subartesian see 2682
-, tapping see 2749

2982 WELL-ALIGNMENT
orderly arrangement of wells in a
linear fashion to produce straight
injection or withdrawal fronts
f   alignement *m* des puits
d   Reihenbildung *f* von Bohrungen;
Brunnenausrichtung *f*

2983 WELL CAPACITY
rate at which water will be yielded
from a well
f   débit *m* d'un puits
d   Brunnenergiebigkeit *f*;
Schüttung *f*

2984 WELL COMPLETION
final cleaning and construction
operations to put well in production
f   complétion *f* des puits
d   Inbetriebsetzung *f* eines Brunnens

2985 WELL CONSTRUCTION
f   construction *f* d'un puits
d   Brunnenbau *m*

2986 WELL CURB
concrete wall around well for
sanitary protection
f   bordure *f* d'un puits
d   Brunnenumrandung *f*

2987 WELL DEVELOPMENT
operations to assure and increase
production of a well before
completing well
f   développement *m* d'un puits
d   Brunnenentwicklung *f*

2988 WELL DIAMETER
f   diamètre *m* du puits
d   Brunnendurchmesser *m*

2989 WELL FIELD
tract of land especially devoted to
wells
f   champ *m* de puits
d   Brunnenfeld *n*

2990 WELL FRACTURING
method of creating fractures around
well by explosion or high pressure
injection
f   fracturation *f* hydraulique des
puits
d   hydraulische Rissbildung *f* in
Brunnen

2991 WELL FUNCTION
exponential integral as used in
Theis' non equilibrium equation;
W(u)
f   fonction *f* caractéristique (de
puits pompé)
d   Brunnenfunktion *f*

2992 WELL HYDROGRAPH
graph of water level fluctuations
in well
f   hydrogramme *m* du puits
d   Wasserstandsganglinie *f* im
Brunnenschacht

2993 WELL INTERFERENCE
effect of overlap of areas of
influence of two or more wells
pumping from the same aquifer
f   interférence *f* de puits
d   Brunnenbeeinflussung *f*;
Übergreifen *n* der Brunnen-
senkflächen

2994 WELL KNIFE
tool to cut perforations or slots
into plain casing
f   coupe-tubage *m*
d   Rohrschneider *m*

2995 WELL LOSS
head loss caused by flow through
screen and inside well
f   perte *f* de charge dans un puits
d   Reibungsverlust *m* im Brunnen

2996 WELL PERFORATOR
tool to produce holes in casing to
permit the entry of water into the
well
f   perforateur *m*
d   Perforiergerät *n*

2997 WELL PIT
well bore, hollow shaft of a well
f   trou *m* de puits
d   Brunnenschacht *m*

2998 WELL POINT SYSTEM
      battery of wells connected by
      suction header
      f batterie *f* de puits
      d Brunnenkette *f*

2999 WELL RECORD
      body of data regarding well
      f rapport *m* sur le puits
      d Brunnenprotokoll *n*;
         Brunnenaufzeichnung *f*

3000 WELL SORTED GRAINS
      assortment of grains having the
      same diameter
      f granulométrie *f* uniforme
      d gut sortierte Kornklasse *f*

3001 WELL SPACING
      distance between wells in a well
      field
      f espacement *m* entre les puits
      d Brunnenabstand *m*

3002 WELL STIMULATION
      well treatment methods to increase
      yield
      f traitement *m* des puits
      d Bohrlochsbehandlung *f* zur
         Erhöhung der Schüttung

3003 WELL TOP
      f tête *f* de puits
      d Brunnenkopf *m*

3004 WELL TREATMENT
      special mechanical or chemical
      treatment of a well to increase
      yield
      f traitement des puits *m*
      d Bohrlochsbehandlung *f*

3005 WELL WATER
      water produced by a well
      f eau *f* de puits
      d Brunnenwasser *n*

3006 WELL YIELD
      quantity of water produced by a well
      f débit *m* d'un puits
      d Prunnenergiebigkeit *f*;
         Brunnenschüttung *f*

3007 WET LINE
      portion of line submerged under
      water in stream measurements
      f câble *m* immergé
      d Unterwasserseil *n*

3008 WETTABILITY
      property of a solid substance to

be wetted by a liquid such as water
      f mouillabilité *f*
      d Benetzbarkeit *f*

3009 WETTED AREA
      cross sectional area of that portion
      of a channel that is filled with water
      f surface *f* mouillée
      d benetzter Querschnitt *m*

3010 WETTED PERIMETER
      perimeter over which the flowing
      water is in actual contact with the
      channel walls and bottom
      f périmètre *m* mouillé
      d benetzter Umfang *m*

      WETTING ANGLE, see angle of contact

3011 WETTING PERIOD
      period of contact between a liquid
      and a solid surface during which
      wetting occurs
      f temps *m* de mouillage
      d Benetzungsdauer *f*

3012 WHIPSTOCK
      wedge-like tool placed in a well in
      order to change the direction of
      further drilling
      f sifflet *m* déviateur
      d Ablenkkeil *m*

3013 WHIRL
      f tourbillon *m*
      d Wirbel *m*; Strudel *m*

      WIDTH, base see 155

3014 WIDTH OF CONTRIBUTION
      width of the contributing region
      between the ground water divide
      from which water enters a well
      (case of originally inclined
      piezometric surface)
      f front *m* d'appel; front *m* d'emprunt
      d Entnahmebreite *f*

3015 WILT, TO
      shrinking of cell walls due to loss
      in turgor as a result of water
      deficiency in plant
      f flétrir
      d welken

3016 WILTING COEFFICIENT;
      WILTING POINT
      f soil moisture content at which
         plants wilt
      f point *m* de flétrissure
      d Welkepunkt *m*

WILTING POINT, permanent
see 2205

3017 WIND FACTOR
factor containing a monthly mean
wind velocity in evaporation
equations
f   facteur *m* de vent
d   Windfaktor *m*

3018 WIND FIELD
air velocity field above ground due
to wind action
f   champ *m* des vitesses du vent
d   Windfeld *n*

WIRE, gay see 915

3019 WIRE GAGE
f   jaugeur *m* à câble
d   Seilpegel *m*

3020 WIRE LINE
wire cable
f   câble *m*
d   Seil *n*; Kabel *n*

3021 WITHDRAW, TO
to draw water from an aquifer or
reservoir
f   soustraire
d   entnehmen

3022 WOLLASTONITE
silicate mineral in contact-
metamorphosed limestone
f   wollastonite *m*
d   Wollastonit *m*

3023 WORKING PRESSURE
f   pression *f* de service
d   Betriebsdruck *m*

3024 WORKOVER
reworking of a well that has
declined in yield
f   reconditionnement *m*
d   Wiederaufwältigung *f*

3025 XEROPHYTE
f   xérophyte *f*
d   Trockenpflanze *f*

Y

3026 YIELD
quantity of water discharged
from an aquifer
f   rendement *m*
d   Ausbeute *f*; Dargebot *n*

YIELD, perennial see 2197
-, safe see 2449
-, specific see 2622

-, sustained see 2733
-, well see 3006

3027 YOUNG'S MODULUS
elastic or stretch modulus giving
ratio of force per unit area to strain
f   module *m* d'élasticité
d   Elastizitätsmodul *m*

Z

ZERO, gage see 807

3028 ZERO ADJUSTMENT
adjustment of a scale or a
measuring circuit to an original
point of departure
f mise *f* à zéro
d Nullpunkteinstellung *f*

3029 ZERO DATUM
f niveau *m* de référence zéro
d Nullhöhe *f*

3030 ZETA POTENTIAL
f potentiel *m* zeta
d Zeta-Potential *n*

3031 ZIRCON
mineral
f zircon *m*
d Zirkon *n*

3032 ZONAL SOIL PROFILE
normal horizontal distribution of
soil zones
f profil *m* de sol à horizons
d zonales Bodenprofil *n*

ZONE, dispersion see 524
-, fault see 710
-, ferrito see 714
-, flushed see 771
-, invaded see 1075
-, littoral see 1160
-, phreatic see 2221
-, root see 2435
-, shattered fault see 2526
-, soilwater see 2602
-, thief see 2775
-, transition see 2820
-, uncontaminated see 2862

3033 ZONE OF ACCUMULATION
second horizon of soil profile (B)
usually zone of clay accumulation
subjacent to zone (A)
f horizon *m* d'apport; horizon *m*
d'accumulation
d Ausfällungszone *f*; Illuvialhorizont *m*; B-Horizont *m*

3034 ZONE OF AERATION
zone in ground profile with
considerable saturation in air where
isolated water moves under gravity
against capillary forces
f zone *f* d'aération; zone *f*
de rétention
d Überwasserspiegelzone *f*;
Haftwasserzone *f*; luftbeein-
flusste Zone *f*

3035 ZONE OF INVESTIGATION
zone over which a given
measuring device is able to obtain
information
f zone *f* d'investigation
d untersuchte Zone *f*

3036 ZONE OF LEACHING
top horizon of soil profile (A) most
intensely weathered
f horizon *m* éluvial; horizon *m* de
lessivage
d Auslaugungszone *f*;
Eluvialhorizont *m*; A-Horizont *m*

3037 ZONE OF RAINFALL
f zone *f* de pluie
d Regenstrich *m*

3038 ZONE OF ROCK FLOWAGE
deep zone of earth's crust where
rocks deform by plastic flowage
f zone *f* plastique de la lithosphère
d plastische Zone *f* der Gesteinshülle

3039 ZONE OF ROCK FRACTURE
upper zone of lithosphere where
rocks react to strain by fracture
f zone *f* supérieure de la
lithosphère
d obere Zone *f* der Gesteinshülle

3040 ZONE OF SATURATION
zone completely saturated with
water, ground water zone
f zone *f* de saturation
d Sättigungszone *f*; Unterwasser-
spiegelzone *f*

FRENCH

F

abaissement de la nappe phréatique 907
- phréatique 2216
abîme 9
ablation 2
abri des pompes 2305
abrupt 2645
absorption sélective 2508
accélération de la pesanteur 879
accident 530
accumulation 14
- d'humidité 2062
acide hydrochlorique 961
- silicique 2547
- sulfurique 2701
acidité 15
acier inoxydable 2637
à-coup de pression 2294
activité induite 1014
- magmatique 997
- volcanique 2902
additif de boue de forage 2084
adhérence du ciment 268
adiabatique 25
adsorption 28
advection 29
aération 30
aérobique 32
affaissement de la surface 1126
affleurement 2146
affluence 1031
affluent 2837, 2838
afflux 1031
- latéral 1134
affouillement 2483
agrégat 35
- des particules de sol 2589
agressif 36
air comprimé 332
aire de drainage 548
- d'influence 107
air-lift 42
albedo 48
alcalinité 54
alimentation 2388
- artificielle 2357
- en eau 2960
- en eau de surface 2726
- initiée 1016
alignement des puits 2982
alios 229
- ferrugineux 714
allochtone 55
alluvion 62
altération des roches 2974
alvéolaire 64
amortissement 67, 436
ampèremètre 65
amphibole 68
amplitude 69
analogie par cuve électro-lytique 342
- par tissu conducteur 343
analyse chimique 284
- complète 330
- de carotte 388
- de l'hydrogramme 970
- fréquentielle 789
- hypsométrique 2078

analyse physique 2225
- statistique 2643
andésite 73
anémomètre 74
angle de contact 75
- de réflexion 77
- de réfraction 78
- de repos 79
- d'incidence 76
anguleux à arêtes vives 80
anhydrite 82
anisotropique 83
année hydrologique 2967
anomalie 87
- de la courbe PS 464
- de la gravité 880
Antécambrien 2284
anticlinal 93
apatite 94
à pente raide 2645
aplanissement 859
appareil de Hele-Shaw 929
- de mesure de la précipitation 2288
- de mesure de l'humidité du sol 2592
appareillage de surface 2716
approvisionnement en eau 2960
aqueduc 98
aquiclude 99
aquifère 2925
aquifuge 102
aquitard 103
aragonite 104
arborescent 460
arbre 2522
ardoise 2568
argile 299, 302
- à blocaux 194, 849, 1162, 2789
argileux 108
argilite benthonique 174
aride 110
arpentage 2729
arrache-carotte 391
arrangement 2166
- des grains 862
- le plus compact 2787
- le plus lâche 1170
arrondi 2442
ascension capillaire 242
atmomètre 118
atmosphère 119
- absolue 4
- physique 4
attraction moléculaire 2066
attrition 120
auget basculeur 2797
augite 122
autochtone 123
avalanche 125
avant-montagne 797
averse 2654
- utilisée dans les calculs 481
azote 2110

bac de classe A 2875
- de décantation 2517, 2577
- de jaugeage 805
- d'évaporation au dessus du terrain 1124

bac enterré 2705
- évaporatoire 681
- flottant 741
- intercepteur 939
bactéries pathogènes 2177
baguette divinatoire 537
baisse du niveau dynamique 562
balance de torsion 2804
balancier 2912
banc de sable à l'intérieur de la boucle 2255
barographe 139
baromètre 140
barrage 435
- déversoir 2158
- souterrain 894
- souterrain en eau douce 792
- souterrain naturel 899
barrière 143
- de perméabilité 2206
- hydrologique 973
- naturelle dans un aquifère 894, 899
basalte 147
basses-eaux 1174
bassin 2845
- clos 309
- de décantation 2516
- d'entremont 1064
- d'épandage 1024
- échantillon 691
- hydrogéologique 895
- hydrologique 2955
- versant 156, 257, 549
batholite 162
bathomètre 163
batterie de puits 2998
berge 136, 643
besoin en eau 2933
béton 338
bicarbonate 176
bief 2421
bifurcation 177
bilan des nappes souterraines 903
- énergétique 649
- hydrologique 974, 2927
- régional 662
biotite 180
bloc affaissé 858
blocage 187
bloc pyroclastique 2313
- surélevé 946
bobine de mesure 2008
bordure d'un puits 2986
borne de mise à la terre 891
- repère 172
bouchon argileux 303
bouclier 2535
boue 2083
- de forage 579
bourbe 2316
brèche 201
bronze siliceux 2549
bruit de fond 128
by-pass 215

cabestan 245
câble 3020
- d'ancrage 915

câble de cabestan 259
- de curage 2462
- de diagraphie 1165
- de forage 578
- de levage 936
- de manoeuvre 573
- de tubage 255
- exondé 43
- immergé 3007
- porteur 251
caillou 2181
caisson 223
cake de boue 724
calcaire 1152
- argileux 109
- d'algues 50
calcareux 224
calcite 225
caldère 226
calibration 227
calotte glaciaire 996
Cambrien 232
camion de diagraphie 1166
- d'enregistrement 1166
canal 277, 2965
- de jaugeage 2009
cannelure glaciaire 848
cañon 234
cap 244
capacité 235
- au champ 716
- capillaire 716
- d'absorption 1025
- de libre écoulement 2622
- d'emmagasinement 2650
- de pénétration 655
- de rétention 2619
- de transmission 2823
- de transport 252, 382
- d'infiltration 1022, 2340
- effective d'absorption 623
capillarité 236
captage d'eau 2928
- des eaux souterraines 896
caractéristiques du bassin 157
- du lit 278
carapace figée 353
carbonate 246
Carbonifère 250
- inférieur 2055
- supérieur 2188
carottage 392
- électrique 633
carotte 387
carte 1185
carter 948
cascade souterraine 897
casque de battage 589
cassure 397
- fragile 205
caverne 260
célérité d'une onde 2972
cellule piézométrique 2291
cendre volcanique 2903
Cénozoïque 272
centre de gravité d'une pluie 274
cercle d'influence 295
chaille 289
chaîne de montagnes 2080

chaleur de condensation 926
- de vaporisation 927
- de vaporisation latente 1130
- sensible 2511
chambre d'aspiration 1040
- de captage 2613
champ de puits 2989
- des vitesses du vent 3018
- vectoriel 2886
changement de faciès 700
charge 922
- accidentelle 697
- admissible 2210
- de dynamite 612
- de la couche du lit 364
- de ruissellement 2917
- du lit 168
- en résidus 2920
- en saltation 2455
- en suspension 2730
- extérieure 697
- normale 153
- permanente 2203
- stabilisée 2101
- sur l'outil 182
- totale 651
charnière 173
charriage 168
chef foreur 576
chemin d'infiltration 2499
chemise de pompe 2310
chenal 913, 2664
- alluvial 57
chevauchement 2162
chloration 291
chlore 292
chott 52
chute 702
- de pression 2292
ciment 265
cimentation 267
ciment d'injection 269
cimenter 266
ciment illuvial 898
circuit de mesure 2007
- intégrant 1049
circulation de boue 2085
- inverse 2405
cisaillement 2527
citerne 296
clapet à échappement d'air 45
- à billes 135
- de fermeture 283
- de fond 774
- de sécurité 2448
- étrangleur 2780
clé à tubes 2241
clivage 306
cloche de repêchage 171
coefficient barométrique 141
- d'activité 23
- d'écoulement 557
- de Darcy 951
- de diffusion 503
- de fluctuation par marées 2784
- de frottement 795
- de fuite 1146
- de l'écoulement total 2447
- de mélange 2057

coefficient d'emmagasinement 2651
- de perméabilité 319
- de perméabilité Darcy sur le terrain 717
- de perméabilité du laboratoire 1113
- de perméabilité relative 2869
- de pondération 2977
- de réduction d'un bac 2170
- de rugosité 2441
- de ruissellement 557
- de stockage 2651
- de traînée 546
- de transpiration 2827
- d'infiltration 2498
- du bac 2170
- du déversoir 2980
- d'uniformité 2867
- hygroscopique 989
coins de retenue 2572
col de cygne 856
colibacille 322
collecteur 2240
- principal 324
collier de battage 590
colmatant 2250
colmater 308
colonne de battage 594
- de boue 2086
- de mercure 2026
- de pierre formée par des concrétions calcaires 587
- de surface 2713
- montante 2413, 2414
compaction 327
complétion des puits 2984
composant 361
composante de gravitation 881
composants volatils 2901
composition 331
compressibilité 333
compteur d'eau 2942
concentration en ions d'hydrogène 965
concession 97
concrétion 229, 339
condensation 340
conditions à la limite 195
- géologiques 830
- de Ghyben-Herzberg 844
- de similitude 2558
- initiales 1034
conducteur 344
conductibilité hydrodynamique 962
- thermique 2768
conductivité 2617
- hydraulique 951
conduit 2239
conduite 345
- d'eau 2946
cône d'alluvions 56, 58, 2747
- d'appel 346
- de déjection 2746
- de recharge 347
- de sondage 592
configuration de drainage 555
- en espalier 2834

interface 1058
interférence de puits 2993
interprétation des diagraphies 1167
interstice de formation 2141
interstices secondaires 2492
intrusion 1072
invasion 1076
- d'eau 2937
- des eaux salées 2491
inversion 1078
iodure d'argent 2557
irradiation solaire 2603
irrigation 1081
isobathe 1084
isochrone 1085
isopièze 1087
isotherme 1090
isotope 1091
- radioactif 2325
isotropique 1092

jaillir 2628
jauge à chaîne 275
jaugeage à gué 2911
- chimique 634
jauge de profondeur 469
- fluviale 469
jaugeur 2010
- à câble 3019
- Parshall 411
jet 1095
jeu du trépan 181
joint 818, 1099, 1100
- de dessiccation 483
- de refroidissement 383
- de stratification 166
- de tige 2799
- d'expansion 690
- fileté 2778
- isolant 1047
- soudé 2981
Jurassique 1103

kame 1105
kaolin 1106
karst 1107

lac 1120
laccolith 1115
- de glace 972, 2235
lac de barrage 2392
- de cratère 399
- intérieur 1039
- salé 2457
lacustre 1116
lac volcanique 2904
lagune 1118
lait de glacier 852
laitier de ciment 271, 2488
laiton siliceux 2548
lame coupante 431
lamination 1122
lapidification 360
latérite 1136
lave à blocaux 188
- en coussins 2233
législation des eaux 2938
lentille d'eau douce 793
- imperméable 1007

lessivage 1142
levé 2728
levée 1148
- de rive 2100
- topographique 2718
liaison hydrogène 964
ligne de base des marnes 152, 2523
- de charge 650, 652
- de côte 316
- de courant 2669
- de crête 404, 552
- de faille 707
- de partage 536, 552, 2955
- de partage entre deux bassins hydrogéologiques 902
- de partage topographique 2800
- de recharge 2358
- de séparation (des eaux) 536
- isohyète 1086
- isoplèthe 1088
- isopotale 1089
limite des neiges éternelles 2583
- de succion 2696
- fixe 734
- supérieure du pergelisol 2201
limnigraphe 2959
- à bulles 206
- à flotteur 740
limnologie 1154
limon 1161
liquide 1155
lissage 429
lit 165, 2660
- d'une rivière 2418, 2663
lithologie 1157
lithosphère 1159
- , zone plastique de la 3038
- , zone supérieure de la 3039
littoral 1160
lobe du glacier 853
loess 1163
log 1164
Loi de Darcy 438
longueur de mélange 2056
lumachelle 386
lysimètre 1175

macropore 1176
magma 1177
magnétite 1181
maille 2029
maillet 2569
maladie d'origine hydrique 2926
manchon de tubage 254, 2238
manivelle 398
manomètre 1184
- à mercure 2027
marbre 1186
mare 2734
marécage 190
- fluvial 2422
marée terrestre 617
marle 109, 1189
marmite torrentielle 2282
marteau pneumatique 41
masse 2569
- tige 569
mât de forage 581, 1196

matelas de gaz 814
matériel non-consolidé 1011
matière en suspension 2731
- polluante 2260
matrice d'outil 2798
méandre 2001
mécanique des sols 2591
médiane 2016
ménisque 2025
mésophyte 2031
mesure 2006
mesures contre les algues 49
métal alcalin 53
météorologie 2035
méthode d'application 2037
- de lavage par contre-courant 130
- des traceurs 2815
- d'infiltration par fossés 533
- d'infiltration par inondation 746
- gravimétrique 884
- numérique 2117
- par bassins d'infiltration 158
- par compression (Mariotte) 816
- par différences finies 729
- par expansion de gaz 816
- par injection de mercure 2028
- par itération 2039
- par remontée 2369
micaschiste 2040
micropore 2042
microtamis 2043
migration 2044
- capillaire 241
milieu aquifère 100
- poreux 2272
minéral accessoire 10
minéraux 2047
- argileux 301
minuterie 2796
Miocène 2052
miroir de faille 2570
miscible 2053
mise à la terre 888, 891
- à zéro 3028
mobile 2846
mobilité chimique 287
- des ions 1079
mode 2058
modèle 2059
- à membrane élastique 2023
- analogique 70
- en sable 2463
modification artificielle du temps 2975
module d'élasticité 3027
mollisol 2068
moment cinétique 2069
monel 2070
monoclinal 2071
montagne tabulaire 2743
montmorillonite 2074
monture 785
moraine 2076

GERMAN

Brunnenabstand 3001
Brunnenaufzeichnung 2999
Brunnenausrichtung 2982
Brunnenbau 2985
Brunnenbeeinflussung 2993
Brunnendurchmesser 2988
Brunnenentwicklung 2987
Brunnenergiebigkeit 2983,
3006
Brunnenergiebigkeitsmass 2614
Brunnenfeld 2989
Brunnenformel, Thiem'sche
2776
Brunnenfunktion 2991
Brunnengleichung, Theis'sche
2767
Brunnen in einem Grundwasser-
stockwerk 2094
Brunnenkette 2998
Brunnenkopf 3003
Brunnenöffnung 2081
Brunnenpfeife 163
Brunnenprotokoll 2999
Brunnenschacht 2997
Brunnenschüttung 3006
Brunnenschutz, sanitärer 2467
Brunnenumrandung 2986
Brunnenwandung 2541
Brunnenwasser 3005

Caisson 223
Canyon 234
chaotische Struktur 281
chemische Analyse 284
- Ausfällung 285
- Mobilität 287
chemischer Sauerstoffbedarf
288
chemisches Äquivalent 286
Chlor 292
Chlorung 291
C-Horizont 293
Colibakterium 322
Cryologie 420
Curie 426

Dach 244
Dachentwässerung 2434
Damm 1148
Dampfdruck 2883
Dämpfung 436
Dämpfungseffekt 437
Darcy 439
Darcy Geschwindigkeit 440
Darcysches Gesetz 438
Dargebot 3026
Daten 441
Dauerfrost 2200
Dauerkurve 609
Dauerlast 2203
Dauerlinie 609
- der Abflussmenge 755
Dauerquelle 2195
Dauerspende 2197, 2733
Deckschicht 2873
Deckschichten 2154
Dehydrationswasser 2945
Deich 505, 1148
Delle 561
Delta 456

Delta-Ablagerungen 457
dendritisch 460
Denudation 463
Desorptionskurve 482
Detritus 486
Devon 488
Diagenese 494
Diaklase 1100
Diamantbohren 495
Diamantbohrkrone 496
Diastrophismus 497
Diatomeenerde 498
Diatrema 2104
Dichte 461, 1192, 2615
dichteste Packung 2787
dichtester Wert 2058
Dichteströmung 462
Dichtung 818, 2165
Dichtungsmittel 2250
Diebszone 2775
dielektrische Konstante 499
- Verschiebung 500
Dielektrizitätskonstante 499
Differentialdruck 501
Diffusion 502
Diffusionskonstante 503
Diopsid 508
Diorit 509
direkter Oberflächenabfluss 5 4
diskontinuierlicher Wert 522
Diskontinuität 521
Diskordanz 81, 520, 2860
diskrete Grösse 522
Dispersion 523
- , hydrodynamische 963
Dispersionszone 524
Doline 538, 2563
Dolomit 539
doppelt wirkende Pumpe 540
Doppelverrohrung 2656
Dosiergerät 711
Dosierpumpe 2036
Dränagerohr 559, 2788
Drehbewegung 2437
Drehtisch 2439
Drehwaage 2804
Drehzahl 2116
Dreirollenmeissel 2841
Drillstemtest 585
Drosselventil 214, 2780
Druck 2289
- , barometrischer 142
- , hydrostatischer 986
- , osmotischer 2145
Druckabfall 2292
Druckaufbaukurve 2290
Druckaufbauverfahren 2369
Druckdose 2291
Druckfestigkeit 335
Druckfläche 2232
Druckgeber 2295
Druckhöhe 641, 922, 2293
- , piezometrische 2230
Druckluft 332
Druckluftpegel 206
Druckmesser 2229
Druckpotential 2231
Druckrohr 518
Druckschreiber 139
Druckstoss 2294
Druckunterschied 501

Druckverlust 923, 2292
Druckwelle 334
Drumlin 599
Dünensand 607
dunkler Glimmer 180
dünner Schuttmantel 61
Dupuit'sche Annahme 608
durchdringbar 2186
Durchfluss 515
Durchflussmessgerät 759
Durchgangsgeschwindigkeit
440
durchgehender Fluss 372
Durchlass 423
Durchlassfähigkeit 382
durchlässig 2186, 2211
Durchlässigkeit, effektive 622
- , relative 2384
Durchlässigkeitsbeiwert 319
- , relativer 2869
Durchlässigkeitsziffer 319
- , ungesättigte 2869
Durchleitung 2822
Durchlöcherung 2198
durchsickern 2192
durchströmen 2192
durchtränkt 2940
Dürre 596
Düse 1095
Düsenmeissel 1096
Düsenstrahlpumpe 1097
dynamische Ähnlichkeit 611
Dynamitladung 612
Dynamometer 613

eckig 80
Effekt, elektrokinetischer 638
effektive Durchlässigkeit 622
- Porosität 624
effektiver Niederschlag 625
- Regen 626
effektive Rückhaltung 620
Effusion 630
Eichfluss 803
Eichkurve 228
Eichung 227
Eigenpotential 2510, 2626
Eigenschaften, elastische 631
Eimer 207
eindämmen 1009
Eindampfungsgestein 685
Eindellung 542
Eindringen 646, 1076
- , vollkommenes ---eines
Brunnen 329
- von Meerwasser 2491
Eindringkapazität 1022
Eindringöffnung 2715
Eindringung 464, 1072
Eindringungskapazität 655
Eindringungsrate 2340
Eindringungstiefe 471, 1077
Einebnung 859
- , seitliche 1133
einfache Abflussganglinie 2559
Einfallen 323, 510
- , ursprüngliches 2140
einfallender Grundwasserleiter
2790
Einfallswinkel 76

Flexur, monoklinale 2071
Fliessbewegung, sehr langsame 402
Fliesschicht 2068
Fliessdruck 757, 955
Fliessdruckmesser 613
fliessen 754
- in offenem Kanal 2131
- von gespanntem Grundwasser 348
Fliessgeschwindigkeit, kritische 412
Fliessgeschwindigkeitslog 767
Fliessrate 761
Fliesstest 764
Fliesswiderstand 763, 2397
Flossverdunstungskessel 741
Flotieren 753
flüchtige Bestandteile 2901
Fluoreszein 769
Fluss 2417, 2662
- , akkumulierender 34
- , durchgehender 372
- , intermittierender 1063
- , isolierter 1045
- , konsequenter 358
- , kurzfristig fliessender 659
- , natürlicher 2102
- , obsequenter 2120
- , perennierender 2196
- , radialer 2321
- , resequenter 2389
- , spezifischer 772
- , subsequenter 26, 2686
- , ungesättigter 2870
- , unterirdischer 2692
- , versinkender 1066
- , wasserabgebender 1032
- , wasseraufnehmender 628
- , wirbelfreier 1083
flussabwärts 541
flussaufwärts 2874
Flussbett 2418, 2663
Flussbettbeschaffenheit 278
Flussschleife 2419
Flussdichte 550
Flussgabelung 177
Flüssigkeit 766, 1155
- , homogene 942
Flüssigkeitsstandanzeiger mit Schwimmer 740
Flusskunde 2275
Flusslauf 2421, 2664
- , antezedenter 90
Flussmorast 2422
Flussmündungsgebiet 456
Flussniederung 193
Flussohle 2420
Flusspat 770
Flussprofil 2671
Flussterrasse 2424
Flussstrecke 2421
Flussstreckenhäufigkeit 2667
Flusssystem 2423
Flutwelle 752
fluviatile Akkumulation 12
Folgefluss 358
Förderdruck 519
Förderrate 2341
Förderseil 936

Formation, lakustre 1117
Formationsfaktor 776
Formationstemperatur 779
Formationswiderstandsfaktor 778
Form des Einzugsgebietes 161
Formfaktor 780
Formveränderung 450
Frachtung, natürliche 2101
Frachtungsfähigkeit 252
freie Oberflächenenergie 786
freies Grundwasser 2859
frei fliessender artesischer Brunnen 756
Fremdbelastung 697
Fremdwasser 1008
Frequenz 788
Frequenzanalyse 789
Frischwasser 791
Frischwasserlinse 793
Fügelmessgerät 428
Führungsschuh 912
Fumarole 800
funikuläres Wasser 801
Furchenquelle 280
Furtmessung 2911
Fussfläche 2182
Fussgranit 162
Fussplatte 154
Futterrohrverbinder 254

Gabbro 802
Galvanometer 809
Gammalog 810
Gang 506, 2888
- , unregelmässiger 2676
Ganglinie der Niederschlags-intensität 987
- des Wasserstandes 969
Gas 812
Gasabscheider 821
Gasausdehnungsmethode (Boyle-Mariotte) 816
Gasaustausch 815
Gasfernleitung 819
gasführend 813
Gasleitung 819
Gaspolster 814
Gassättigung 820
Gasspeicherung im Wasser-träger 101
Geber 2817
Gebietsbilanz 662
Gebirgskette 2080
Gefäll 702, 2573
geflutete Zone 771, 1075
Gefrierprozess 354
Gefrierpunkt 787
Gefrierzone, jährliche 84
Gefrornis 2200
Gegendruck 129
Gegenstrom 396
Gegenstromspülung 2405
Gegenströmung 396
gegrabener Brunnen 605
Gehäuse 948
Gelände 2761
Geländeneigung 890, 2387
Geländeoberfläche 889
Geochemie 824

Geodäsie 825
Geohydrologie 827
geohydrologische Einheit 826
Geologie, tektonische 2679
geologische Beeinflussung 831
- Korrelation 832
geologischer Schnitt 829
geologisches Log 833
geologische Verhältnisse 830
geometrische Ähnlichkeit 835
geometrisches Mittel 834
Geomorphologie 837
Geophon 838
Geophysik 840
peophysikalische Exploration 839
geothermisch 841
geothermischer Gradient 842
gerammter Brunnen 591
Gerinne 768
Geröllfrachtung 2455
Gesamtabfluss 2666, 2810
Gesamthärte 2807
Gesamthöhe der Energielinie 651
Gesamtporenraum 2808
Gesamtporenvolumen 2808
Gesamtproduktion 424
Gesamtverdunstung 658
Gesamtwasserverbrauch 363
gesättigte Strömung 2469
Geschiebebelastung 364
Geschiebefracht 168
Geschiebefrachtung, hüpfende 2455
Geschiebelehm 194
Geschiebemergel 849, 2789
geschweisster Tuff 2314
Geschwindigkeit 2889
- , Darcy 440
Geschwindigkeitshöhe 2890
Geschwindigkeitslog 18
Geschwindigkeitspotential 2891
Gesetz, Darcysches 438
gespanntes Grundwasser 349
Gestalt, kugelförmige 2624
Gestängetest 585
Gestängeverbinder 2799
Gestein 2426
- , anstehendes 169
- , kavernöses 262
- , klastisches 298
- , kristallines 421
- , verfestigtes 359, 1019
Gesteinsbildung 494
Gesteinsfolge 2430
Gesteinsformation 2429
Gesteinskunde 2212
Gesteinstextur 2432
Gestell 785
gestörte Probe 531
Getriebepumpe 823
gewachsener Fels 2856
Gewässerkunde 977
- , beschreibende 971
Gewässernetz 554
Gewässerschutz 2263
Gewicht, spezifisches 2618, 2978

Gewichtszahl 2977
Gewindeverbinder 2778
Gewitter 2654
Geysir 843
Gezeitenschwankung 2785
Gezeitenstrom 2783
Gezeitenwirkungsgrad 2784
Ghyben-Herzberg'sche
  Bedingungen 844
Gipfel 2703
Gipfellinie 404
Gipfelpunkt 403
gitterförmige Anordnung 2834
Glazialablagerung 845
Glaziologie 854
gleichförmig 941
gleichförmige Strömung 2866
Gleichförmigkeitsziffer (nach
  Hazen) 2867
gleichmässig 2865
Gleichstrom 512
Gleitfrana 615
Gletscher 851
- , aktiver 21
Gletscherablagerung, alluviale
  56
Gletscherfurche 848
Gletschermilch 852
Gletscherschutt 846
Gletscherspalte 408
Gletscherzunge 853
Glimmer, dunkler 180
Glimmerschiefer 2040
Glückshaken 869
Gneiss 855
graben 504, 687
Graben 532, 858
Grabental 2410
Gradient 861
- , geothermischer 842
- , hydraulischer 954
Granat 811
Granodiorit 866
Grauwacke 886
Gravimeter 876
gravimetrischer Feuchtegehalt
  877
Greifbagger 297
Grenzbelastung 2673
Grenze, festgelegte 734
Grenzfläche 366, 1058
Grenzflächenspannung 1059
Grenzsaugfähigkeit 2696
Grenzschicht 196, 350
Grenzwert 1153
Grobkörnigkeit 313
Grobsand 312
Grobsplitt 419
Grösse, diskrete 522
- , skalare 2475
Grosspore 1176
grösster Reliefunterschied 1198
Grotte 260
Grube 2242
Grubenabflusswässer 2045
Grubenwasser 2049
Grubenwässer 2045
- , saure 17
Grundeis 72
Grundgestein 169

Grundgleichung, hydrologische
  976
Grundkomplex, kristalliner 145
Grundlast 153
Grundmoränengeschiebe 1162
Grundmoränetümpel 2734
Grundquelle 2681
Grundwasser 892
- , Fliessen von gespannten ---
  348
- , freies 2859
- , gespanntes 349
- , künstliches 2360
- , schwebendes 2190, 2876
- , unechtes 1060
- , ungespanntes 2859
- , ursprüngliches 2097
- , vadoses 2876
- , wiederkehrendes 2402
Grundwasserabbau 2051
Grundwasserabfluss 910
- , unechter 2690
Grundwasserabsenkung 907
Grundwasserabsenkungskurve
  908
Grundwasserader 893
Grundwasseranreicherung,
  induzierte 1016
- , künstliche 2357
Grundwasseraustritt, flächenhafter 2501
- , natürlicher 2098
Grundwasserbarriere 894, 973
Grundwasserbecken 895
Grundwasserbestandsaufnahme
  903
Grundwasserdargebot, sicheres
  2449
Grundwassereinzugsgebiet 895
Grundwassererhebung 905
Grundwassererschliessung 896
Grundwasserfliessgeschwindig-
  keit, tatsächliche 720
Grundwasserfluss, ungespannter
  2858
- mit freier Oberfläche 765
Grundwassergleiche 1087
Grundwasser im Permafrost-
  bereich 1070
Grundwasserleiter 100
- , artesischer 113
- , einfallender 2790
- , küstennaher 314
- , leckender 1147
Grundwasserneubildung,
  künstliche 117
Grundwasseroberfläche 2219,
  2962
Grundwasserprovinz 906
Grundwasserreservoir 909
Grundwasserscheide 901, 902
Grundwassersohle 1171
Grundwasserspeicher 909
Grundwasserspende 900
- , künstliche 116
Grundwassersperre 102, 899
Grundwasserspiegel 904, 2962
- , schwebender 2191
Grundwasserspiegelabfall
  2216

Grundwasserspiegelanstieg
  2218
Grundwasserstandsmessgerät
  163
Grundwasserstauer 99
- , begrenzt durchlässiger 103
Grundwasserstockwerk 2093
Grundwasser über der Ge-
  frornis 2710
Grundwasserüberfall 897
Grundwasser unter der
  Gefrornis 2685
Grundwasserzement 898
Grundwasserzone 2221
Grünsand 887
gut sortierte Kornklasse 3000

Haarriss 2041
Haff 1118
Haftwasserzone 3034
Hahn 318
Halbwertszeit 916
Halteseil 915
Haltungsvermögen 2403
Hang 2573
- , ansteigender 11
Hangrutsch 1125
Härte 920
- , bleibende 2202
- , permanente 2202
- , temporäre 2756
- , vorübergehende 2756
Häufigkeit 788
Häufigkeitsanalyse 789
Häufigkeitsverteilung 790
häufigster Wert 2058
Hauptschieber 822, 1183
Häutchenwasser 2183
Hauteffekt 2566
Hebekappe 937
Hebekran 938
Hebevorrichtung 1093
Hebewerk 565, 935
Hebewinde 935
Hebung 2872
Heilquelle 2017
Hele-Shawmodell 929
hervorquellen 2628
heterogen 930
Hochebene 2246
Hochscholle 946
Höchstwert 2178
Hochwasser 743, 933
Hochwasserabfluss 932
Hochwasserberechnungs-
  grundlage 480
Hochwasserlängsschnitt 749
Hochwasserscheitel 745
Hochwasserschutz 744
Hochwasserspuren 747
Hochwasserweiterleitung 750
Höhe 640, 922, 1149
- des Salzgehaltes 2453
- des Wasserspiegels 2631
Höhenlinie 374
Höhenmarkierung 172
Höhenschichtlinie 374
Höhenverteilung 106
Höhle 260
Höhlenkunde 2623

Meereshöhe, mittlere 2004
Meeresspiegel 2487
Meerwasser 1187, 2124
Meinzereinheit (USA) 2019
Meissel, stumpfer 606
Meisselkörper 2798
Meisselschneide 290
Meisselspiel 181
Melioration 2363
Membranmodell 2023
Membranpotential 2024
Mengenlinie 1191
Meniskus 2025
Mergel 109, 1189
Mesophyte 2031
Mesozoikum 2032
Messband 2748
Messchacht 806
Messelektrode 2278
Messflügel 2438
Messgerinne 2009
Messkabel 1165
Messkreis 2007
Messlänge einer Anordnung
  2609
Messlatte 2012, 2630
Messpule 2008
Messrinne 2010
Messtank 805
Messstation 808
Messstelle 695
- , hydrometrische 980
Messung 2006
Messwagen 1166
Messwarte 808
Messwehr 2014
Messwinde 2011
Messzylinder 2013
metamorphes Wasser 2033
meteorisches Wasser 2034
Meteorologie 2035
Methode, numerische
  (Lösungs-) 2117
- der endlichen Differenzen
  729
Mikrolog 365
Mikropore 2042
Mikrosieb 2043
Mineralien 2047
Mineralöl 2046
Mineralquelle 2048
Minimalereignis 2050
Miozän 2052
mischbar 2053
Mischlänge 2056
Mischverhältnis 2057
Mitnehmerstange 1109
mit Schichteinschaltungen
  versehen 1051
Mittel, arithmetisches 111
- , geometrisches 834
mittelkörniger Sand 2018
Mittelwert 2005
mittlere Meereshöhe 2004
mit Zwischenmitteln versehen
  1051
Mobilität, chemische 287
  der Ionen 1079
Modell 2059
Modellverfahren 2060

Modellversuch 2061
mögliche Evapotranspiration
  2279
Molekulardiffusion 2067
moleku e Anziehungskraft
  2066
Monel-Metall 2070
monoklinale Flexur 2071
monomolekulare Schicht 2073
Montmorillonit 2074
Moor 2075
Moräne 2076
Moränenablagerung 2077
Moränenschutt 2077
Morast 2316
morphometrische Analyse 2078
Mulde 2740, 2845
Muldenquelle 468
Muldental 2739
mulmig 794
multiple Reflexionen 2095
Mündung 644, 674
- eines Entwässerungsgebietes
  159
Mure 2089
Muschelkalk 386
Mutterboden 2802
Mutterlauge 2079
Mylonit 2096

Nachfall 264
Nachfolgefluss 2686
Nachfolgetal 2675
Nachfrage 458
nachgeräumter Brunnen 2346
Nachschneider 2347
nahtloses Rohr 2489
Natrium 2588
natürliche Frachtung 2101
natürlicher Fluss 2102
- Grundwasseraustritt 2098
natürliches Wasser 2103
Nebenfluss 2837, 2838
Neigung 860
Neigungsmesser 1010
Nennlast 2203
Nettoeinstrahlung 2105
Netz 2106
Netzpunkt 2111
Neutralitätspunkt 2107
Neutronenlog 2108
Neutronenquelle 2109
nicht bodenständig 55
- mischbar 1002
nicht zusammenhängendes
  Material 1011
Niederschlag 2285
- , effektiver 625
- , konvektiver 379
- , orographischer 2142
- , zykonaler 434
Niederschlagberechnungs-
  grundlage 481
Niederschlag auf Wasser-
  flächen 279
Niederschlagsbeobachtungsnetz
  2332
Niederschlagsfall
  2654
Niederschlagsfülle 13

Niederschlagsgebiet 549
Niederschlagshöhe 472
Niederschlagsmesser 2112,
  2288
Niederschlagssammler 2652
Niederschlagsschreiber 2366
Niederschlagssumme 13
Niederschlagsüberschuss
  2287
Niederschlags-Verdunstungs-
  verhältnis 2286
Niedrigwasser 1174
Niedrigwasserabfluss 1173
Niveau, piezometrisches 2232
Nonius 2892
Normale 2113
normale Verwerfung 2115
- Wassertiefe 2114
Nullhöhe 3029
Nullpunkteinstellung 3028
numerische Lösung 2118
- (Lösungs-) Methode 2117
nutzbare Kapazität 124
Nutzwasser 1021

Oase 2119
obere Permafrostgrenze 2201
- Zone der Gesteinshülle 3039
Oberfläche, spezifische
Oberflächenabfluss 2159, 2446,
  2721
- , direkter 514
Oberflächenabsenkung 1126
Oberflächenenergie, freie 786
Oberflächenfilm 2717
Oberflächenhaftwasser,
  zusammenhängendes 801
Oberflächenrückhaltung 2714,
  2720
Oberflächenspannung 2724
Oberflächenspeicherung 2714
Oberflächenverkleinerung 2712
Oberflächenwasser 2725
Oberflächenwasservorräte
  2726
oberirdisch 3
Oberkarbon 2188
Oberlauf 924
obsequenter Fluss 2120
Obsidian 2122
ofentrocken 2152
offenes System 2132
Ölbohrung 2127
Ölfeldwässer 2125
Oligozän 2128
Olivin 2129
oolithisch 2130
Optimierung 2134
Ordnungsstufe eines Flusses
  2670
Ordovizium 2135
organischer Inhalt 2137
organische Verunreinigung 2138
organogene Ablagerung 2136
Orientierung 2139
orographischer Niederschlag
  2142
Orthogonalität 2143
Ortstein 229
Oser 673